Leap to Freedom

Marjorie McKenzie Davis

Acknowledgments

I want to thank the following people for their help and advice from their varied and unique perspectives:

My daughter, Janet Prince. Without her love and encouragement I would not have attempted to write this book. Her professionalism in all fields, from journalism to graphics design, guided me from a small beginning to the finished product.

My son, Joseph Saitta, media consultant. His love, support, unique advice, and vision remained constant throughout this writing.

My editor, Jerry Parker. A special thanks for his professional dedication.

And to my friends whose enthusiasm, suggestions, and opinions were of so much value. Thanks to each of you.

The Department of Fish and Game California
Code of Regulations

While laws concerning wildlife are primarily designed to protect wildlife and preserve native species, there are exceptions which allow for rescue of injured animals, scientific study, and educational use of wild animals. These exceptions require official permits.

Section 251.7 Title 14

Except as otherwise authorized, it shall be unlawful for any person to possess any live native wildlife except wildlife temporarily confined to treatment or care if the animal is confined at a Department-authorized wildlife rehabilitation facility or organization.

Leap to Freedom

True stories of wildlife rescue and rehabilitation, including

Deer Gabriel

Marjorie McKenzie Davis

Burley Creek Studio

ISBN 0-9667286-0-2
Library of Congress Catalog Card Number: 98-91743

Published by Burley Creek Studio, Annapolis, Maryland
Printed by United Book Press, Inc., Baltimore, Maryland

These are stories based on true accounts. Names and places have been changed.

Cover & book design by Janet Prince
Front cover photos by Amanda Kreglow
Back cover photo by Janet Prince
Chapter sketches by Marjorie McKenzie Davis

For information, please contact Marjorie McKenzie Davis, P.O. Box 5, Kenwood, California 95452, or Burley Creek Studio, P.O. Box 1987, Annapolis, Maryland: voice & fax:410-757-4455.

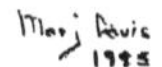

To my two yearlings,
my daughter Janet,
my son Joe.

Contents

Part 1

Deer Gabriel

Part 2

Wildlife Rescue

Part 1

Deer Gabriel

The Fawn

There it was I saw what I shall never forget
And never retrieve.
Monstrous and beautiful to human eyes,
hard to believe,
He lay, yet there he lay,
Asleep on the moss,
his head on his polished cleft small ebony hooves,
The child of the doe, the dappled child of the deer.

Edna St. Vincent Millay

Introduction

There is a longing within most of us to have a true understanding of natural wildness. My hope is to bring to the public a new way of looking at wildlife.

Deer Gabriel, based on a case study, brings one well-loved species familiar to us all into a closer view. It explains a wild animal's need for freedom. Making pets of these creatures of the wild, exploiting them for whatever purpose, poaching, destroying their habitat, and insisting that they conform to the human idea of wildness are but a few of the unacceptable negatives that need sincere consideration and a fresh perspective.

Countless other fascinating experiences, each containing a lesson about wildlife, are logged in the files of Wildlife Fawn Rescue ready to be shared.

M.D.

1
In the Glen

Only the deep resonant "whoo-hoo-hoo" of the Great Gray Owl breaks the intense stillness. Moon rays shimmer through the trees, illuminating the floor of the dense Sierra forest. Countless nocturnal creatures, accustomed to sensing rather than seeing, move silently along crisscrossing paths as they retreat to the security of nests, dens, or beds for the daylight hours. A compact cover of low woody vegetation and tightly matted shrubs offer a shield from danger. The approaching dawn triggers the cycle anew. A feathery mist floats high, dissolving in the light of the morning sun that radiates over the mountain ridge.

The ancient forest stirs. The hush of night gives way to the soft chirp of awakening birds. A hungry hawk circles widely on morning patrol, searching for movement in the meadow below. Others, wings outspread, perch high on the tips of the redwoods, catching the early warmth of the sun.

Nearby, a weary doe lies resting. Rosy shafts of sunlight creep slowly across the meadow reaching into her quiet haven, warming the still moist body of her newborn fawn. Gabriel nestles tightly against her, listening to the beating of her heart and the rhythm of her breathing. He derives comfort from her closeness. He is new to the world and she is all he knows of it. He presses his nose beneath her flank to suckle hungrily.

The doe, roused from fatigue and free of her burden, feels her strength returning. Her deep brown eyes open slowly. She lifts her head to catch the whispers of the woodland creatures as they skitter and scurry, intent on their morning errands. Familiar sounds echo through the still dark woods and move across the air. The doe contentedly nuzzles her fawn. She will stay close, nurturing him throughout his first day.

Gabriel was born with his eyes open to greet the world. His fragile body is covered with hair to provide warmth. Although well able to stand within minutes after birth, his hoofs are still too soft and tender, and his slender legs too weak to allow him to follow his mother on her search for the succulent food she must find to provide the rich nourishment crucial to their survival. This richness enables Gabriel to go for long intervals between feedings.

He slumbers through his first days while his mother wanders the meadow rim to browse. Upon awakening he can see her through the branches, sampling the tender shoots, or drinking from the nearby stream.

Gabriel has become familiar with the quiet spot in the wilderness that is his home. Warm and well hidden he listens to the leaves rustled by a gentle breeze. He smells the air sweetened by the scent of fir. He studies a line of busy ants ascending the curve of a lichen-covered log. A spirited hare springs from cover, close to where he lies. Gabriel peers through the brush to watch as it hops from place to place, cropping the emerging buds with great efficiency. Intrigued, he rises awkwardly to his feet and stumbles forward. The startled hare bounds into the tall grass and is gone. The fawn samples a few bites of violet leaf, sniffs inquisitively at a burrowing beetle, then returns to his bed to wait for his mother. At sundown he arises to watch expectantly as she suddenly appears through the trees. The doe patiently stands as he nurses, then lies by his side to rest for the night. Close by a gray fox, alert, hesitating, ventures from her den as the light fades, warily leading three eager kits into the glen for their evening hunt.

Sunlight ascends over the crest of the hill, heralding another day. The doe gracefully stands and stretches languidly. She gazes down at her fawn and pushes her nose into his side to encourage him to get up. Gabriel, having gained better control of his spindly legs, stands swaying before her. He ducks beneath her flank to nurse.

After making certain that her fawn has eaten enough to last until her return, the doe methodically licks him from head to tail. He must be free of scent as he lies unprotected at the base of the tree where she will leave him while she goes off to forage. He inches forward and closes his eyes as she licks.

Each day her fawn must be hidden in a different place as a precaution against predators, even though he, as yet, has no natural odor to attract them. Already accustomed to this early morning routine he moves unsteadily to the spot she has chosen. Low hanging boughs of flowering dogwood nestle beneath the shade of a giant conifer. Red sorrel peeks through many layers of soft dark mulch. California Buckeye, richly adorned with creamy outstretched blossoms, poise gracefully along the forest fringe. The beige, yellow and brown colors of new growth conceal the spotted hair of the fawn.

Satisfied that he is comfortable and well camouflaged, she reaches down, nuzzles and licks his uplifted face once more, then turns to walk across the meadow. His soft dark eyes follow her as she disappears over the rise. The sun will be low on the horizon when she returns.

Settling in for the day, he closes his eyes. The air smells sweet and the humid scent of the earth beneath him is reassuring. A narrow stream sparkles its way over sun-warmed stones, lending its murmur to the soothing sounds of the forest as they drift in and out of Gabriel's consciousness. He soon falls into a deep sleep.

The weight of this five-pound fawn will double in two weeks. In three weeks he will be gamboling in the meadow with other fawns, flipping and leaping into the air with delight, landing with a twist on all four feet, his hoofs hardened and his legs quite strong. Gabriel's mother will no longer have to leave him behind as she forages. Together they will walk into the meadow to graze where blue lupine, buttercups, and nodding columbine open their faces toward the morning light, and tender shoots of wild oats sway gently in the lush grassland.

As Gabriel dozes, far down the other side of the lofty mountain Reed Jones pulls into a small parking area. The trapper grabs his gear and sits on a rock to change into his hiking boots. Hoisting the backpack to his burly shoulder, he fastens the waistband and adjusts the strap. Since he plans to be gone most of the day, he moves quickly to his truck, tosses in his driving shoes, rolls up the windows, and locks the doors.

The trapper frowns as he begins the long climb up the steep trail. The spring day is unseasonably hot. The sultry, humid air guarantees him a laborious ascent. The seldom used pathway provides no shade. He curses the irritating burrs that grab at the legs of his pants. Near the top he rests and drinks from his canteen, as he surveys the dense forests, lush meadows and sparkling lakes stretching in a broad panorama below.

Its beauty awakens in him no feeling of oneness with nature. His quest is not for beauty. Reed mumbles to himself, as his practiced eye focuses his binoculars on a well-worn path leading to the lake shore. "I'll check those traps and be out of this heat by noon. Should be a good day." He stands up, stretches and returns his canteen to the backpack. "With luck I'll find a nice healthy fox waiting for me this time, or even a bobcat. I sure could use the cash."

In spite of his caution as he enters the deep woods the ground crackles sharply beneath his boots. His presence is an intrusion in a wilderness seldom invaded by man. The forest becomes silent. Small creatures scurry at his approach. The strident voice of the Steller's Jay grows still. The low hoarse croak of the frogs ceases abruptly. Soundlessly, they slip into the nearby pond.

Reed moves from spot to spot, exchanging old bait for new, as he inspects each of the traps he had so painstakingly set. He is irritated to find he has made the long, hot climb for nothing. He swears under his breath as he heads back through the woods toward the trail.

Gabriel awakens with a start. His sensitive ears pick up this disturbing new sound. He raises his head apprehensively. Instinctively he quickly flattens his small body tightly against the earth. His spotted hair blends perfectly into the leaves and moss surrounding him. He lies motionless, barely breathing, his eyes large with fear.

The man passes without seeing Gabriel, so expertly is the newborn camouflaged, yet something catches his eye. The filtered sunlight shimmers on the fawn's soft brown hair. Reed stops and turns to look more closely. He bends quickly, scoops up Gabriel and hoists his five-pound body high into the air.

Gabriel screams. His sharp shrill cry pierces the hushed quiet of the forest. Wild creatures freeze in their hiding places. Fear radiates throughout the once-peaceful woodland. He screams again in terror. The poacher grins as he reaches back to pull a burlap sack from his backpack. He stuffs Gabriel into the sack and tucks it under his arm.

As they move down the narrow path Gabriel kicks and struggles to be free. The poacher holds him more tightly. "What luck!

I thought it would be a good day, but this was almost too easy," he laughs triumphantly. "Okay bud, settle down. We've got a hot hike ahead of us." Completely exhausted, overcome with fear, Gabriel finally lies quietly under the man's arm. The stench of the human body burns his sensitive nostrils. The sound of the human voice grates alarmingly in his ears.

Rounding the last switchback, the poacher scouts the view for hikers. He is relieved to see no other vehicle down in the parking lot. Approaching his truck he glances nervously in every direction before unlocking the door. Quickly he pulls his illegal bounty out of the sack, tosses him carelessly into a cardboard box, and closes the lid tightly. Gabriel trembles in the total darkness that envelops him. The box reeks with the fetid odor of other creatures that have made this same distressing journey before him.

Reed slides hastily into the driver's seat, slams the door shut, and turns on the ignition. The forceful roar of the engine and the vibration of the moving truck causes Gabriel to scream once more and kick frantically at the sides of his prison. His energy spent, he collapses, hopelessly hugging the floor of the box, his tiny heart pounding in terror.

*

The last light of the afternoon sun washes over her gleaming brown hair as the doe steps into the glen. She halts, detecting the still strong scent of a predator—man. Though she is frightened, she moves boldly into the meadow and advances silently and cautiously to where she had left Gabriel. Her fawn is gone.

She searches desperately throughout the moonlit night, knowing his spindly legs cannot carry him far. She pushes her nose into every crevice where he might be sleeping. She pauses to check behind each log over which he may have stumbled and into narrow ravines where he may have fallen. As the hours pass, her pace slackens, her head lowers in defeat, and she ventures no farther. The soft yellow light of dawn is reflected in the grief-filled eyes of the doe as she reluctantly makes her way back into the glen.

2
Animal World

The building was a dented Quonset hut near the outskirts of Rosemead, graying and rusted with age. It had been abandoned after World War II. The town slowly spread out around it. Each time it changed hands the front of the building acquired a new look. Now the hodgepodge entry displayed a glaring sign, ornamented with cartoon characters, garish orange and pink colors, and large glossy black letters. "FREE! See the WILD BEASTS OF THE FOREST in Animal World."

Animal World was part of a popular and growing trend. Native wildlife cannot be sold legally, but these businesses gain a state permit using the stratagem of rehabilitation. As a privately owned business, Animal World worked under contract to the bustling city of Rosemead in Southern

California. Rosemead had no established agencies, such as Animal Control or a Humane Society responsible for collecting stray domestic animals. Animal World captured these homeless animals then sold them for a nominal fee. Exotics stolen from their homeland, were shipped to this facility under stressful conditions, and then bred. Their young were domesticated and sold at great profit.

Daily the crowds poured in the front entrance to view the wildlife on display. A side door led potential customers into a spacious room filled with a variety of domestic and exotic animals. Impounded dogs and cats, unwanted rabbits, goats and reptiles, various rodents, and colorful birds huddled miserably in stacked, cramped cages along the exit corridor. Animals on exhibit sold briskly to the eager visitors. The success of Animal World gratified its owners.

*

The poacher's truck halted abruptly outside the back gate to Animal World. The box containing the dazed, frightened fawn hurtled forward on the seat. Reed made a quick grab to prevent it from tumbling to the floor of the truck. He leaned on the horn. Gabriel cowered and trembled in terror as Reed shouted, "Hey! Open up! It's hot and I'm in a hurry. Me and this little buck here got some important business with Pruitt."

A shoddy, unkempt man in filthy jeans that were torn and splattered with stains, sauntered around the corner of the shed. His sandals flopped loosely from feet caked with dust and grime. Squinting in the brilliant sun, he pushed limp hair from his eyes to peer in the direction of the truck. "Reed? You're back early. A buck you say?"

"Yep. Wait 'till you get a look at this prize," Reed smirked.

As the gate swung open, Reed's friend peeked inside the box. "Earned your money this time, eh? Kinda cute. Be a big hit with the customers. Stop by for a cold drink after you collect." He stepped back into the shade of the shed as he pulled off his sweat-soaked T-shirt. "How'd ya like this heat today?"

Reed pulled the truck to a stop just inside the large back yard of the compound, parking among the dust-covered boxes, crates, cages and animal carriers tossed carelessly behind the small shed. Foul-smelling, unemptied litter boxes, food-encrusted feeding trays, and rubbish-filled plastic bags formed cluttered piles under the overhang. Flies buzzed over it all. Dusty bags of dog and cat food, rabbit pellets, sacks of grain and seed filled the small shed to overflowing. A mouse scurried for cover. Heat from the blazing sun pulsated on the metal roof.

The poacher climbed down out of his truck, grabbed the box containing the fawn, and with a bold, arrogant stride headed down the maze of halls. Without waiting for an answer to his knock, Reed pushed open the door to Carl Pruitt's office. Planting the box on the manager's desk, he said, "Cash on the line, Carl. The price of wildlife just went up."

After a quick inspection of the box, Pruitt leaned back in his chair, lit a cigarette and grinned, "A mule deer! A little buck at that. I am impressed, Reed. This time you outdid yourself. I can already see the customers lining up to get a look at it." Pruitt stood up, walked around to the front of his desk and shoved Gabriel's box to one side. "Got time for a cold beer?" he asked.

"Sounds good. It was hot up there. And I mean hot! I wasn't prepared for that kind of heat this time of year." He popped the can and guzzled several huge gulps. "Got my traps reset. The place seems to be teeming with wildlife this year. Tracks everywhere. So I don't understand why none were sprung. Must be the heat, I guess. Still a good spot to remember." He plunked the crumpled can on the desk, and wiped his mouth on his sleeve. "Okay. Gotta run. Just give me a call."

Pruitt smiled broadly as he counted out the bills. "Worth every dollar." Then he added, "This enough?"

"For this time," Reed laughed, as he stuffed the cash into his pocket and turned toward the door.

Pruitt dismissed the poacher with a casual wave, stamped his cigarette into the floor and quickly turned his attention toward Gabriel. He buzzed for the attendant who hurriedly entered the smoke-filled room. "Get this animal out of this box before he dies on us," he ordered.

The attendant picked up the container holding the frightened and dehydrated little deer and carried him into the wildlife section of the building. Gabriel had been without nourishment since early morning. His five-pound body had no reserves to combat the heat or the hunger. He lay listless and weak. His empty stomach told him that it must be time for his mother to be back. He longed for the comfort of her closeness, and for her rich warm milk. He yearned for the shelter of his haven in the glen.

The attendant glanced at his watch. "Time to get outta here," he grumbled. He quickly examined, weighed, and dusted the distraught fawn with flea powder, then impatiently shoved a bottle of strange tasting formula into his mouth. Desperate for food, Gabriel drank. With no thought for this innocent animal in his care, the attendant put his charge back into the dirty box and pushed it under a table for the night. "See ya in the morning, guy. Sweet dreams." The weary young captive trembled in the darkness, longing for his mother.

Early the next morning the attendant, still groggy with sleep, pulled the box containing the wild-eyed but submissive fawn from under the table and fed him. He hoisted the box onto his shoulder and carried Gabriel into the wildlife section. "Here's your new home, guy," he said, placing the fawn in a small narrow run that was enclosed with heavy wire. Fetid odors of previous animal occupants still lingered. A water pan occupied one corner of the pen.

The zoo keepers housed all wildlife in one section—predator and prey. Bobcat, red fox, coyote and raccoons; owls, falcons and kestrels; squirrels and hares; and now a fawn huddled side by side in individual enclosures. Their natural instincts in such close quarters compounded their stress.

Mammals enclosed in small runs paced endlessly. The cages provided no tree limbs for climbing, no hiding places for the timid, displaced, and frightened creatures. Day after day tethered raptors languished on posts above the animal section. The wild creatures cowered submissively in their cages and pens. Many perished as the result of stress. They were quickly replaced.

The unnatural formula, lacking the richness of his mother's milk, caused Gabriel to be ill for many days. Diarrhea and dehydration drained his strength. He stood with head held low, his thin back hunched in pain. Having no mother to lick and clean him, his small body became soiled and rank.

He curled listlessly against the fence of his pen. The presence of other wildlife did nothing to comfort him.

The wildlife section of Animal World opened promptly at ten o'clock. The public streamed by, commenting on an individual animal or bird that they viewed. As Pruitt predicted, Gabriel proved to be a great attraction. But the unfamiliar odors and the confusion of sounds made it difficult for him to adjust. A child rushed impetuously to the pen, grabbing and shaking the fence vigorously. "A deer, Mommy, a deer," he yelled. "Come'ere, deer, come'ere. Do you like chocolate?"

His horrified mother pulled him back quickly. "No, Artie, get back. That's a wild animal. He'll bite your hand off. Come on, let's go buy the little duck you wanted." The group surrounding them laughed indulgently. Gabriel pushed his small body tightly against the far side of his pen, trying to distance himself from the chattering, noisy crowd.

Eventually, however, the small buck became accustomed to his imprisonment, and most of all, the human contact. He stood quietly gazing back through the fence at the daily visitors. His initial fear of his surroundings subsided and he finally came to accept his new way of life. Day followed day. Weeks became months. Gabriel, now four months old, was fully weaned. His spots had faded and small pedicels, from which his antlers would grow, emerged on each side of his forehead.

Even though Gabriel had never enjoyed tasting an acorn, or tearing a prickly leaf from a live oak, or splashing along the rocky banks of a stream to drink from its cooling waters, he was, nevertheless, born wild. His instincts developed normally. He showed no fondness for his captors, never advancing toward them in recognition or friendship. One morning, as the attendant approached with the cleaning hose, the growing deer stepped forward aggressively with his head lowered. He forcefully stamped his front hoof in warning. The surprised attendant backed away and quickly headed in the direction of the manager's office. "Mr. Pruitt," he said, as he shook his head. "That young buck just challenged me. He's no threat at his age, but I thought I'd better let you know."

"Well, this is as good a time as any to have him neutered," answered Pruitt with a shrug. "Got to think of the liability, you know." Hoping to calm the growing deer's aggressive behavior, Pruitt contacted their vet. Several days later the doctor entered Gabriel's cage, tranquilized him, and performed the surgery.

Gabriel spent the first year of his life at Animal World. The soft fragrant earth, the warmth of the sun, the fresh cooling rains, the sweet smell of grass, and the joyful melody of birds faded from his memory. The maturing buck grew unhealthy and thin. The meager diet of alfalfa did not provide the extensive variety of natural browse needed to sustain a healthy deer. His hair became dull and matted. His pen, barely larger than a standard dog run, lacked the space for the quickly growing yearling to develop muscle and strength. His hoofs, unable to wear down in the normal manner, grew long, splayed apart and curling upward, making it uncomfortable for him to walk on the hard concrete.

*

A recent article in the entertainment section of the local paper described the newest attractions to be seen at Animal World. Jean Taylor, a retired biology teacher who donated time and money to many worthy animal organizations was prompted to visit the wildlife section of Animal World just before closing time. Pleased to have the place to herself, she leisurely passed by each cage, observing the wildlife without distraction. She soon became aware of the misery projecting from the eyes of each of the animals. Massive-winged hawks with no room to spread their wings, no space to soar, huddled in parrot cages. "Horrible," she murmured as her eyes filled with tears.

"This is just horrible," she whispered, gazing at the tethered owls that peered down at her, silently clinging to their overhead perches. Sensing their constant stress, she spoke to them gently. "Why are you here?" Tears flowed down her cheeks. "Do you still have strong memories of flight? Have you forgotten the rush of the wind on your wings?" Overcome with both grief and rage, unable to advance to one more cage, she ran toward the exit, stumbling in her haste, never glancing at the extensive array of domestic animals that she passed on her way to reach the door.

Early the next morning Jean Taylor picked up the phone and called the California Department of Fish and Game.

3

The Department of Fish and Game

Department of Fish and Game Patrol Captain Leo Bateman listened carefully as the young woman voiced her concerns. Still disturbed by her traumatic experience of the previous day, Jean Taylor questioned the ethics and the policies behind this wildlife exhibit.

"The conditions at Animal World are intolerable," she said. "I'm not an expert, but even I could see that the animals are not properly cared for. They're listless and unhealthy looking. They have no reason to live. Have you ever seen the place?" Not giving the captain time to reply, she continued, "Isn't there a law against confining a wild creature for life? Who issues these permits? Who inspects these places? The filth, the cramped cages, the misery in the eyes of each of them kept me awake most of the night. Captain Bateman, you must get someone down there to do something about it."

Captain Bateman assured her that no policy existed that permitted the conditions she described. "We'll get right on this, Miss Taylor," he said. "I'll admit I haven't seen the facility you mention. It's funny, the name doesn't even ring a bell, and it should. Give me your number and I'll get back to you. Thanks for calling in this report. If the conditions are as bad as you say, I promise we'll take quick action."

"What was that all about?" asked Warden Venta, who had been listening nearby.

"Maybe nothing, Steve, but it sounds as though this woman has a legitimate complaint. We'll soon find out." He swiveled his chair to face the computer terminal and punched up the complete listing of permits currently active in their region of the state. After considerable checking and rechecking, he whistled softly and murmured, "No permit. Nada. I wonder how long they've been in operation."

"Hard to tell. These places seem to spring up overnight," the warden replied. "And in our large territory they're not easy to find."

"True, but people like Miss Taylor can be a big help in bringing them to our attention. It was good to talk to her. She spoke with intelligence and authority. It's not easy to understand wildlife. They don't adapt well to captivity—something wild in their nature still struggles to be free," said the captain. He picked up his notes, adding, "Well, I'd better get this report to Tracy. You know how he loves going after these guys."

Lieutenant Phil Tracy, area supervisor, took charge of the investigation. After intensive research Tracy's team finally acquired the authority to move in and shut down the compound. They obtained the necessary warrant for the search of Animal World's premises and the confiscation of all native wildlife.

The morning of the raid Captain Bateman, behind the wheel of the Department of Fish and Game transport truck, glanced at his partner, Warden Steve Venta, and grinned. "This looks like a big one. I hope you had a good breakfast this morning. I have a hunch it'll be a long time before lunch."

The warden chuckled, "I'm prepared. I've stashed coffee and donuts under the seat. That's about as close to hearty as I get." Glancing over his shoulder while fastening his seat belt, he asked, "Did you get a look at the backup? Tracy's got three more trucks with another eight wardens behind us. And he said a city patrol car will meet us in Rosemead. He says it's a big compound."

After driving in silence through the busy city streets, the warden continued, "I've never been to Rosemead. I thought I knew our region pretty well, but this Animal World is one that slipped by all of us."

"Sure did," agreed Bateman. "Rosemead is more than a hundred miles north of here. It's right in the heart of the San Gabriel Valley. These days one town blends right into the next. No way to tell where one ends and another begins unless you keep your eye out for those little signs, 'Welcome to So-and-So, Population 85,000.' Maybe they felt safe up there, since it's not a city you'd be going to without a reason. No beaches." He paused to look out the window at the slow-moving traffic. "We have a lot of territory to cover in the name of wildlife. If these businesses don't file for a permit, we have to wait for something like this to happen."

As the traffic opened, they picked up speed. The steady motion of the truck relaxed the two men, and they settled in for the long drive ahead. Venta interrupted their short silence. "I was just thinking, Leo. At one time the names of these towns we're passing through had meaning. Orange, for instance. Whatever happened to the miles of orange groves that once lined these roads?" He didn't wait for an answer. "When I was a kid, I loved sticking my head out of the car window to smell the spring blossoms. Me and my dog—his ears flapping in my face," he sighed. "Remember how green everything was around here then? The open fields, green hills, native trees and brush?" His partner nodded. "Housing developments and strip malls have taken over most of the southern part of the state. What was the name of that song of the 60's? Something about chopping down a tree and putting up a parking lot? It makes me cringe when I think of all that's gone forever."

"I hear ya," said Bateman. "And wildlife is disappearing along with its habitat. As Chief Seattle once said, 'Whatever happens to the beasts, soon happens to man.' A lot of wisdom in that. What a guy he must have been. Did I ever tell you that he was my childhood hero?"

"Really? That figures, I guess. None of us would be in this job if we didn't love nature."

"Yep. I remember pretending that I was a Navajo sheepherder of long ago, rambling through the red hills, or camping along the banks of the Colorado River—roaming free and sharing the land with every other living creature. Why can't it still be that way?" Bateman asked. They turned silent, each lost in his own thoughts.

A few miles down the highway Venta continued the theme. "Yes, the world is changing, and we can't go back. Along came the population explosion, the destruction of the environment, and all that followed. Looks like we may all be headed for big trouble, doesn't it?"

"You're so right," Bateman chose his words carefully because of the message he wanted to get across. "Then came the need for regulations and controls. That's when the Wildlife Conservation Departments emerged as the nation's regulatory bodies for the management of wildlife. What a great job we have—to be entrusted with the responsibility to investigate and enforce all violations against wildlife." He cut his speech short when he saw the large Animal World sign ahead glaring in the brilliant sunlight. "Well, hold that thought. We're here. Are you ready for some action, Warden Venta?"

"Ready, Captain."

Their arrival startled Carl Pruitt as he leaned against his office doorway, just finishing the last drag on his cigarette. Flipping the butt to the ground, his eyes widened as the convoy of trucks, led by a city patrol car, swung into the driveway of his compound. Pruitt's heart raced. His mouth went dry as he nervously twisted his lips into a smile of welcome.

Lieutenant Tracy left his truck and briskly walked up to the balding man. "How are you this morning, sir? I'm looking for Mr. Carl Pruitt, the manager of Animal World."

"You found him," he said coldly. "Need something?"

"Just your cooperation, Mr. Pruitt." Handing Pruitt the search warrant, Tracy continued. "We've come to remove all wildlife from these premises. We'll be closing you down."

Pruitt glanced at the warrant. "No! You're making a big mistake, officer. You can't just come barging in here without warning, like in some TV movie," he protested. "I'll get the owner down here right now and we'll straighten this mess out, but fast!" Sweat beaded on his face.

"We've got our..."

Pruitt interrupted Tracy. "We're a legitimate business, here. You guys drive up like Elliott Ness and think you can just come in and take over the place? Well, forget it!" His strained voice pitched higher as he raged. "I'll get my boss on the phone. He'll take care of your complaints."

"That may ..."

"Mr. Craiger has lots of influence around this town, as you'll soon find out."

"That may be, Mr. Pruitt," replied Tracy. "But we intend to move these animals out. Now." The lieutenant signaled the wardens and police out of their vehicles.

Ten wardens and three police officers filed into the compound. "Go straight to the back. Check all the doors as you go," Tracy called to the men.

Pruitt grabbed the phone and furiously dialed Craiger's number. "Yeah, Pruitt here. We've got a problem, Mr. Craiger. A big problem. It's like a war zone down here. Uniforms swarming all over the place. Department of Fish and Game, cops, the works. They're cleaning out all the wildlife. Can they do that? I tried to stop them. Yes, of course they have a warrant. What do I do 'til you get here?" He listened eagerly for instructions. "Okay, okay. Better hurry." He slammed down the receiver and rushed after the wardens.

Red faced, the manager pushed his way through the men to find Captain Bateman and Warden Venta testing a locked door. He made one last effort to convince Lieutenant Tracy to wait for the arrival of the owner. Tracy answered with an order, "Break it down."

"Okay. Okay. Will ya hold it?" shouted Pruitt. "We don't want the door in splinters." He unlocked the door and stepped aside to allow the raiding party to enter the wildlife section of the compound.

Bateman pushed the door open and stepped into the dimly lit room. The men crowded behind him to stand silently staring at the scene before them. Lack of sufficient ventilation made the stale air difficult to breathe. Bird droppings coated the floor under the cages that hung from a metal bar to the left of the room. A red fox huddled in a run that reeked of stale scraps of dog food. The dirty walls surrounding it all were splattered from years of careless cleaning. Drains were girdled with waste.

Swiftly calculating the number of animals, the lieutenant said in a carefully controlled voice, "Venta, take charge of getting those transport carriers back here as quickly as you can. These animals have spent too long in this awful place already. Let's move them out." His loathing glance covered the room once more. "I've seen enough." He turned to Bateman. "Oh, and have someone call headquarters to tell them that we'll be here for the rest of the day. There's a lot to do."

Bateman walked quietly among the animals while waiting for the transport cages. In a far corner he came upon the enclosure housing a young deer. Cautiously, the captain entered the stall that had been Gabriel's home for nearly a year. As he knelt to the level of the deer, the half-grown emaciated buck advanced to nuzzle the hand that gently stretched toward him. Bateman swore softly to himself as he ran his hand along the animal's protruding rib cage. He felt beneath his flanks. He stood slowly and left the pen as Gabriel watched pensively.

"Tracy, we've got a yearling mule deer back here. A neutered buck, at that. Must have been brought down from the High Sierras. Came a long way, that little guy. There's nothing but Black-tails in this area. This would be a good animal to hold as evidence." He walked back to rub Gabriel's head gently. The young deer stood quietly, displaying no instinctive fear of these men. "Look at him. He's sure been handed a bad deal in life. He's so badly imprinted that it will be impossible to ever release him."

As the two men moved away from Gabriel's pen, Bateman said, "He's all I'll have room for in my truck. Steve and I should be able to get up to headquarters by tonight if we leave now."

"Right," Tracy answered. "My plan is to move all the animals to licensed wildlife care centers throughout the region where they'll get the professional help they need. I'm hoping most of them will be releasable after they've had time to adjust." Tracy turned to glance at Gabriel. "Leo, why don't you locate Steve, have someone else take over the distribution of the crates and cages, and get on your way. Get this little buck into the truck and take off. Let me know how it goes. Call headquarters before you leave, explain the situation, and tell them to expect you."

Tracy scowled as he surveyed the room full of apprehensive wildlife. "I'll have misdemeanor charges filed against the operators of this place within the week," he vowed. "We've surely got all the evidence we need to file a strong case against them."

Bateman and Venta gently guided Gabriel out of the pen. Barely aware of his surroundings, the languid yearling followed the men out of the gate. They expertly lifted him into the truck, secured the door behind him, and were on their way. Gabriel stood swaying unsteadily in the back of the paneled vehicle as it picked up speed. Wearily, he lowered himself down onto the padded floor where he dozed during the long trip to northern California.

*

Darkness closed in, and a driving rain pelted steadily against the truck windows as Gabriel and his exhausted rescuers pulled into Rancho Cordova headquarters, bordering the Sacramento River. On rare occasions, such as this, it becomes necessary to move a wild animal into the Department of Fish and Game's wildlife facility. Large animals, captured for various reasons, are housed here.

Bateman and Venta guided the still drowsy young buck out of the truck and into the dry, clean stall which would serve as his temporary living quarters. He seemed unaware of the other deer occupying nearby stalls.

Quite early the next morning, the refreshed yearling discovered the open door leading to an exercise area. He hesitated just inside his stall, then cautiously stepped through the gate, pausing once more before venturing farther. He raised his head to sniff the air, picking up the strong scent of the nearby deer. Genetically programmed with a need to be among his own species, Gabriel took several eager steps in their direction. The temptation to make contact with these familiar smelling creatures was strong, but his instinct warned him to be wary. He circled with caution, breathing in the scent that aroused this primitive urge, then stood motionless as they approached to touch noses. A large doe planted a hoof sharply on his shoulder to indicate that she was in charge. In confusion, Gabriel shied away. However, the resident deer soon adjusted to the newcomer, and Gabriel quickly learned to yield to the doe's leadership. He settled into a close companionship with his own species at last.

*

Lieutenant Tracy lost no time in filing a misdemeanor charge against Animal World with the County Municipal Court, listing illegal possession and mistreatment of wildlife.

News of the raid promptly spread throughout the Rosemead community. An article appeared in a local morning paper, "State Wardens Raid Animal World," it screamed. Not completely understanding the issue, a public outcry against the Department of Fish and Game arose. A deluge of calls and letters flooded the Department with demands and threats. The public proclaimed the 'right' to have wildlife displayed for their enjoyment.

Finding public sympathy in their favor, the owners of Animal World quickly took advantage of the situation, hoping to regain possession of the wild creatures which provided an enormous attraction for their business. During interviews, Craiger claimed rightful ownership of the animals that he insisted had been stolen from his facility. He played the role of the injured party with skill, falsely declaring that the animals would be killed by the Department. Craiger filled the media with misinformation.

In rebuttal, the Department of Fish and Game issued a news release outlining the reasons for their action. To solicit support from other sources, the Regional Patrol Chief, Warren Rogers, phoned friends involved in the care of wildlife. Maggie McKenzie, director of Fawn Rescue in Northern California, received his late afternoon call with pleasure. "Maggie, I seem to remember that you have been active in a few wildlife issues in the past. Haven't you written some articles defending the Department's stand on wildlife protection?"

"That was a while back, Warren. You have a good memory." Maggie laughed.

"I've been thinking, Maggie, that it would be nice to have some positive letters, written by experienced wildlife people, explaining why it's important for us to rescue captive native animals. It's hard to reach the public on these sensitive issues, and difficult to convince them that wildlife belongs to no one. The Department is assigned to protect wildlife. That's our job."

"I'll do what I can," she said. "I'll get a letter in the mail right away. Send me a copy if it gets printed. I'm so far north that I never see a Southern California paper." She wished him luck.

Maggie wrote, in part: "The exploitation of wildlife for private gain must not be tolerated. The animals that were confiscated by the Department of Fish and Game were found to be improperly caged and deprived of the natural diets that are essential to their health. They were carelessly housed near domestic animals that are capable of harboring diseases known to be fatal to wildlife. The Department had no alternative but to move decisively toward the rescue of these animals. It is the duty of the Department to protect these wild animals." Maggie urged the public to stand behind this positive action. "Strangely," she continued, "humans are fascinated by wildlife because they are wild. At the same time, they refuse to acknowledge that keeping these animals captive deprives them of that very wildness that they so admire."

Both Animal World and the Department of Fish and Game awaited their day in court.

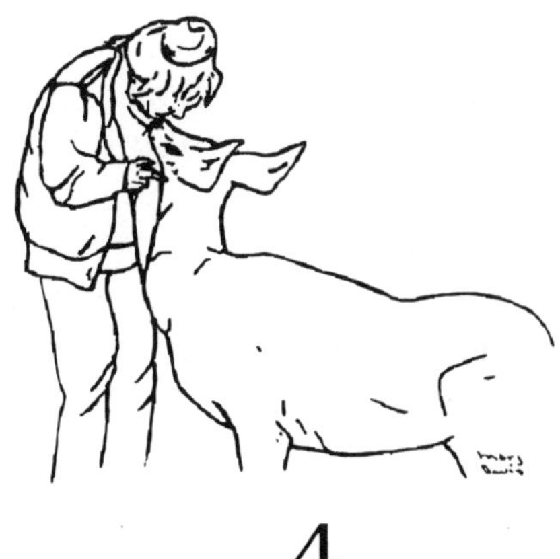

4

A Chance Meeting

Due to the nature of her work, Maggie McKenzie normally worked alone, giving protection and care to orphaned, ill, or injured wildlife—a twenty-four hour commitment requiring skills and stamina. It was her custom to respond to emergencies without delay. Fawns and automobiles collide too often in the predawn hours. Dogs released to roam after dark become packs and often bring down deer.

High on a deeply wooded hill overlooking the tranquil Valley of the Moon, an hour's drive north of San Francisco, Fawn Rescue's secluded outdoor shelter provides the necessary privacy that is vital to a fawn's survival. This refuge gives fawns freedom to roam and to learn the ways of the wild before they can be safely released. For this reason, the facility is kept off limits to the public.

No other center in Northern California specialized in the care of fawns, and although Maggie's original intent was to confine her volunteer rescues to Sonoma County, fawns began to filter in from farther and farther away. An overnight trip to the central valley, a six-hour drive in blinding rain, or a back-road journey along a foggy shore no longer seemed unreasonable.

On rare occasions, Maggie offered internships to local university students, as well as volunteers from animal care facilities. At this time Beth Warner, a biology major, worked with Maggie.

Orphaned fawns whose mothers have died, or ones removed from their resting spot by well-meaning humans, arrived daily and needed immediate nourishment. While Maggie examined and weighed the fawn and entered the information on the record sheet, Beth prepared the formula. As Beth reached into the dishwasher to pull a spotless bottle from a tray of twenty bottles, she said, "Good grief, Maggie, do you use all of these bottles at one time?"

"You bet—sometimes even more. New fawns drink only four ounces of formula. However, the older ones are already demanding twelve ounces. As they grow that will increase to two full eight-ounce bottles. That's a lot of weight to carry down those long steps. Good exercise, though. I never put on a pound during fawn season,"

Maggie laughed. "I have a friend who constantly complains about the high cost of weight-loss programs. I tell her that getting involved with wildlife will solve her problems, but she's not convinced that it's her type of commitment." She showed Beth how to mix the fawn's formula.

"Now, this formula is the equivalent of the doe's milk. That's why it works," she explained. "The actual milk of a doe was analyzed by a national laboratory. Each year they manufacture enough Doe Milk Replacer to provide proper nourishment for all the orphaned fawns in the United States. It can't be bought from a feed store. It has to be ordered directly from the lab. As you know, a fawn can die from being fed cow's milk or human foods."

"Tiny four-pound fawns like this little gal have no reserves, do they?" asked Beth.

"No, they don't. So it's crucial that we get these babies at once. Every spring we try to get the message out that people should not try to raise fawns on their own." As she spoke, a phone call came into the facility with an urgent plea to help an injured fawn.

This was the busiest part of the season, which made Maggie a familiar figure at Dr. Patton's veterinary clinic a few miles up the highway. The clinic's staff expected to see her daily, rushing in with her white hair flying and her jeans stained with blood. Today was no exception.

"What is it today, Maggie?" asked the concerned receptionist. "From the looks of you, it must be serious."

"A little doe was hit by a car and thrown into a ditch. She can't stand. She's in shock. I've still got her strapped in the stretcher," Maggie explained.

"Fine, one of the girls will help you carry her in. I'll tell Dr. Patton you're here. He'll get her stabilized and into X-ray."

"Thanks, but I don't need help," Maggie replied. "Beth is with me today. We can handle it." Maggie raced back outside to her truck. The two women quickly pulled the stretcher from the camper and hurried into emergency, then awaited the results.

Dr. Patton showed Maggie the X-rays. "They clearly show the pelvic injury," he explained. "She'll do fine. She's young and her bones will mend quickly. Let her move as she pleases, but keep her fairly confined in the holding pen until she heals. Then she can join the roughnecks," as he called her healthy, active fawns, "until she's old enough to release."

Grateful and relieved, Maggie thanked the doctor, who responded modestly, "We do what we can. You bring them in. I fix them up. That's the way it works." This compassionate young vet donated his services as his contribution to the needs of wildlife.

Too often at Fawn Rescue, calls come in from irate citizens, such as a recent call from a wealthy retiree. "Fawn Rescue? This is

Sylvia Beck. I need advice. Several deer are making a path right through my lawn. What can I do to stop them? And don't tell me to build a fence. I've already been given that advice by my neighbor. I don't want a fence on my property. I just want these animals to go some place else."

Maggie patiently began, hoping to convert, "Wild animals don't intend to destroy your property, Mrs. Beck. They only want to pass by quietly. Your yard is simply one more step along a path they've traveled for centuries. They can't read the 'No Trespassing' or 'Don't eat the roses' signs."

"You've got that right," interrupted the caller. "They're demolishing my roses."

Maggie continued, ignoring the interruption,"Many people travel thousands of miles on vacation just in hopes of seeing wildlife, while we have them in our back yards every day. We consider it a privilege to watch these graceful, gentle creatures at such close range," she said. "At this time of year they even bring their babies when they feel secure enough. A rare treat. Have you seen any babies this year, Mrs. Beck?"

"Well, yes, I have. Darling little things," she replied, softening her attitude, as had so many other callers in the past. "You're right, of course. I'm a city gal. I moved to the country recently to enjoy the beauty. The first thing I do is complain. I have a lot to learn, don't I?"

"Just enjoy wildlife while they still share our land," said Maggie. "And you're right about not wanting that fence. There are too many as it is, aren't there?"

Maggie leaned back in her chair, pushed the loose strands of her long hair back into its top-knot, and laughed. "You get the next one, Beth. You never know what's on the other end of the line. But I do prefer a complaint to an injury call. Those are never easy."

"I'm still learning how to deal with the public," Beth replied. "I sometimes wonder if I'll ever learn all there is to know. Why do you do it, Maggie, year after year? How many years has it been? Ten? Twelve? You're seventy-six years old now, and show no signs of slowing down. What makes you keep going?"

"Well, I'll admit that sometimes I find myself out of gas and running on fumes, but I guess what really keeps me going is that I'm needed. It's nice to be needed no matter what age you are," Maggie said reflectively. "Just wait until fall, Beth, when you look back and remember all the injections you've given, the fawn with pneumonia, and the one with the leg ripped open on the fence. You'll be hooked, too. How about the time we got up at 2:30 a.m. to pick up the one hit by a car? These experiences can't be paid for in wages. They make us forget the hard work and stress. Maybe it's my small way of giving something back to a world that has given so much to me." Beth agreed.

Maggie continued, "I learned long ago that dealing with helpless wildlife is a stressful, frightening experience for the general public. They can't, by law, keep them in their possession, so there's a real need for wildlife centers. And Fawn Rescue fills such a need. It takes a lot of common sense, and an instinct for wildlife to do this work. If you can't think wild, you might as well get out of the business. I have no patience with what the Department calls bunny huggers."

"Bunny huggers?"

"You've seen them—the ones who coddle and cuddle the cute babies, but cringe at fleas, ticks and blood. By the time you train them and they find out it's not all petting and bottle feeding, they're gone."

"I'll have to admit I had no idea that in addition to the regular routine there are long anxious hours of vigil, months of gathering fresh greens in the heat and many miles of transporting to get the job done," Beth said.

*

Maggie worked under a special permit issued by the Department of Fish and Game. Soon after the raid on Animal World she received an invitation from the Department to attend a series of classes that would increase her skills in handling deer. She accepted without hesitation, explaining to Beth how important she felt it was to continually search for any available means to increase her knowledge about the species that she has chosen to rehabilitate. Classes, literature, and personal experience all provided valuable information. So Maggie rearranged her schedule for the following week.

On the second day of attendance, after a series of lectures, the students advanced to working directly with an animal related to their specialty. Maggie was assigned to one of the smaller deer. As she entered the enclosure with her instructor, Jim Graham, the yearling trotted up to greet her. As he lifted his face to hers, she remarked with astonishment, "He sure is friendly. I've had tame fawns, but I can't remember one quite as tame as this little guy. He's a mule deer, isn't he? Where did he come from? Why is he here?"

"We got him from Rosemead, down in the San Gabriel Valley. He no doubt originally came from the High Sierras, since we have only Black-tails in the area where he was being held captive. We're holding him as evidence. The charges are unlawful possession and mistreatment of wildlife," Jim explained.

Maggie stared at Jim in astonishment. She had no doubt that this was the same yearling that she had recently written about in the paper at the request of Patrol Chief Rogers. And now destiny had brought Maggie and Gabriel face to face. For what reason, Maggie wondered, as she tried to compose her emotions. A powerful connection, a special bond, drew her to this captive young deer. During the instruction she felt compelled to ask more about plans for his future after the trial. "Where will he go?"

Jim had no answer. "Unfortunately, there is no place for an imprinted, neutered deer. We can't keep him here."

"Has anyone ever tried working with a deer with these handicaps and made a successful release?"

"Never," replied Jim. "We lack the personnel, the time, and the facility to even consider it. We're just not set up for it."

"How about letting me have him?" asked Maggie. "He deserves a chance at life. How do you know it can't work if it's never been tried? Let me take him to Fawn Rescue," she persisted. "I've had success releasing tame fawns. Many times, when the fun of bottle feeding is over, fawns are brought to me by bored people just wanting to be rid of them. In the past these fawns were considered unreleasable and were routinely euthanized," she said, trying to persuade him. Not giving him time to respond, for fear he would turn her down, she continued with her new and radical proposal. "This is one reason Fawn Rescue was founded—to try to find new answers, to try new techniques." He nodded in agreement. Fueled by a positive sign, Maggie added, "Over the years I've learned to put these tame fawns in with ones who are nearly ready for release. And then I withdraw all human contact. They relate only to their own species and are eventually released with the others. I've had good follow-up on them. They've been seen, their tags shining in the sun, still together in a herd. It works."

"Oh, sure, Maggie," laughed Jim. "You want us to just turn this yearling buck over to you? It's not that simple."

"Well, don't just say no. I only want you to plead my case to the Department. Let me try. Sure, I might fail. If I do, I'll let you know. But what if it works? Think of what we will have learned. This young buck has been through so much turmoil caused by all the human interference. He deserves a chance at freedom," Maggie pleaded. She realized that it was a remote possibility that she would ever see the yearling again.

"I'll give it my best shot," promised Jim. "Just don't get your hopes up."

At the conclusion of the series of classes, as Maggie gathered her papers and books and prepared to leave, she thanked Jim for inviting her to the class. "These new techniques will help me in my rescue work," she said. "Especially when I'm called to pick up a fawn that turns out to be a full-grown buck with a good sized set of antlers. It does happen. Oh, and let me know about the San Gabriel Valley yearling."

Weeks later, after the Animal World trial, Jim called Maggie with an update. "A favorable decision for wildlife," he said. "But, that's not my department, so I don't know all the details. My responsibility is moving this young buck out of headquarters. Were you serious when you offered to take him?"

"The San Gabriel Valley yearling? You bet!"

"He's yours, then. If you're willing, we're willing."

"I'll be there in the morning with the truck. What time will you be there? How early can I come?" Maggie asked.

"No, we'd better bring him to you. Your truck might not be secure enough to protect either of you. I'll meet you on the highway near Fawn Rescue, and you can guide me in."

In a burst of joy Maggie blurted out the news to Beth. "Beth!" she shouted. "Jim just called from headquarters. He's bringing the San Gabriel yearling..." she thought for a second about what to call him. "Gabriel. Gabriel is coming to Fawn Rescue tomorrow—his first step to freedom."

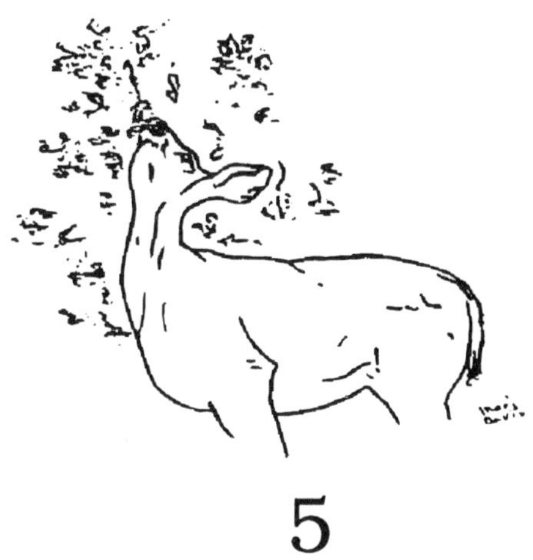

5

A First Step

Now Maggie faced a serious new challenge. The abrupt arrival of the yearling meant finding precious space among pens filled with young fawns. Traditionally the busy season at Fawn Rescue begins during the chilly days of March. The incoming four- and five-pound newborns require warm formula, heating pads and indoor shelter until they are stabilized. One fragile three-and-a-half-pound orphaned baby more closely resembled a stuffed toy than a living deer. Fawns continue to arrive at a steady pace during the spring months. This year, by mid-June, twenty-seven fawns of various ages and sizes filled Fawn Rescue's pens to overflowing.

Maggie talked through her dilemma with Beth. "I don't dare risk mingling the two age groups, even though the yearling seems tame and gentle. My first consideration must be the safety of the fawns. Nevertheless, Gabriel's needs are important, too. We have only one day to come up with a solution."

From Maggie's recent visit with Gabriel, she knew that he was now a true yearling, a spike, already several months into his second year. She remembered how proudly he stood, head erect, to display a pair of three-inch velvet-covered antlers. Although his health had improved steadily, he still needed time to adjust and space where he could run free. He needed adult nourishment and conditioning to the wild. Maggie knew his long convalescence required wide-open spaces that were not available at her facility this time of year. "The facility at Fawn Rescue is definitely out," she explained to Beth. "However, there is Molly's ranch and it's only an hour's drive north. I set up a satellite there several years ago that contains two sections, one for fawns and the other for older deer."

"Will she be willing to help?"

"Most likely she will," Maggie continued. "I take partially tame fawns there to learn to be wild." Once these special fawns became accustomed to the new area, they were free to wander in and out though the open gate. Molly provided food and water for them as long as they continued to return. Gradually the fawns withdrew from security, preferring the freedom of the wild countryside. She had recently converted a large five-acre parcel of vacant horse pasture to house the older deer. "We have three deer there now that are nearly ready to be free. The ranch might be ideal for Gabriel."

Maggie called Molly to propose the idea. Molly answered without hesitation, "Bring him up here. The others are about ready to go. We have plenty of room. That small buck that was so badly injured has healed well. He welcomed the two young does you brought to join him. Probably lonesome. There's no reason to think they won't accept your yearling. They're all close to the same age."

"That was my thought, too," said Maggie. "I don't want to overload you, but I was hoping you would agree. And I should mention that Gabriel is very tame and needs a lot of help. It will be a long time before he's ready for release."

Molly didn't hesitate to welcome Maggie's new yearling. "Well, then it's settled. He's welcome for as long as it takes." No one could have guessed the length of Gabriel's stay.

*

The early morning fog clung to the floor of the valley where Maggie and Beth waited for Gabriel's arrival. Like a ghostly apparition, the Department of Fish and Game truck emerged from the haze and came to a halt by the two women standing along the roadside. Maggie introduced Beth to Jim and explained their change of plans as they climbed into the truck.

"We aren't going to Fawn Rescue after all," she said. "While we still have the yearling in the back, we might as well take him up to Molly's near Cloverdale."

Jim liked the idea. A four-hundred acre hilltop ranch sounded like the ideal spot for Fawn Rescue's special cases. "I've been wanting to see the place ever since you began taking fawns up there."

On the way north Maggie described the overloaded pens at Fawn Rescue and why Molly's ranch was the ideal location. Gabriel would regain his wildness at the ranch and then be released there. He would not have to be moved again. The arrangement seemed foolproof.

Jim turned off the highway and onto the dirt road that led to the ranch. Stands of fir rose gently along the boundary. Glimpses of a trickling stream sparkled in and out beside the twisting road. Tangled wild grape vines wound through the brush, nearly covering the russet branches of the abundant madrone trees. Masses of poison oak showed spots of vibrant gold and brilliant red among their shining green leaves. As the truck slowly climbed the final steep grade, a squirrel scurried erratically in front of it. Jim braked and swerved to miss the critter. A wild turkey fluttered over the fence and onto the low-hanging limb of an oak. "Wow, what a spot." said Jim. "I could settle in here for life. Isolated and wild. I can't imagine a better home for this deer. Looks like his problems finally are over."

"And ours, I hope," added Maggie.

A feeling of excitement was shared by Gabriel and his delivery team as they entered the gate to the ranch. Gabriel smelled the tantalizing freshness of the morning air. Tired of the long confining drive, he pawed the sides of the crate impatiently.

After Jim backed the truck tightly against the open gate leading to the five fenced areas, the group carefully slid the large wooden crate out of the truck and lowered it to the ground.

"I wondered how we would get him down," laughed Maggie.

"It's all leverage. No lifting at all," Jim explained, as he pried off the back of the crate and stepped aside. "Here we go, little buck. Look at all that open space."

Gabriel hesitated at his first encounter with freedom. No crowded concrete pen. No constraining wire fence. Just acres of open space. Although he was free to exit the crate, as his hoofs touched the soft grassy soil, he halted abruptly. He nosed the fresh warm earth, breathing in its humid scent. He pawed, testing its consistency. He reached to nibble a blade of new growth, tasting for the first time the succulent sweetness of wild grasses. He turned toward the water trough to drink deeply, satisfying his thirst after the long transport.

Gabriel darted wildly up an incline and through the open field of high grass. This field, spreading before him in all directions, gave Gabriel the space he needed to run, tall grasses in which to lie in comfort and security, and a natural habitat where he could become familiar with other creatures of the wild. He stopped to raise his eyes in wonder at a hawk circling gracefully overhead.

Maggie and Jim walked to the crest of the hill searching for the three deer that had vanished instantly into the trees when they arrived. Knowing the deer would not show themselves while humans were near, Maggie and Jim moved slowly toward the gate. Gabriel and his new companions would introduce themselves when they were gone.

As they left the ranch, Maggie felt satisfied that Gabriel had taken his first important step toward the life he had been born to live—a free and wild existence. She glanced back in time to see him tear a sharp succulent oak leaf from a dangling branch, then lift his head high to reach a hanging acorn. One day, thought Maggie, he will lie beneath the protection of that same thick cluster of live oak during the cooling rains. But for now, she felt content to know that tonight the yearling would sleep, for the first time in his memory, under a shimmering starlit sky.

6

A Time for Learning

Two days later, just after sunrise, Maggie answered Molly's desperate call. "Maggie, you've got to get up here right away. Gabriel has been severely injured, and I don't know what to do." She cried hysterically.

"How badly is he hurt? What happened?"

"The other deer must have attacked him. I found him when I came down to put out their feed this morning on my way into town. He's mangled and torn. He's bleeding. Hurry, Maggie, please." Before Maggie could respond, Molly continued, "Oh, this is awful. I have an important meeting, and I'm already late. I can't miss it. I have to leave right now. I'm sorry I can't be here to help you. Can you get someone to come with you?"

Maggie assured her that she would leave immediately. She called Beth and arranged to pick her up on the way out of town. "I'll be waiting outside," said Beth. "What do I wear?"

"Just boots and working clothes. I have all the equipment ready to go." Maggie pulled on her jeans, boots, and sweatshirt and raced out the door. Satisfied that all her emergency equipment—stretcher, blankets, and medications—was in order and secured in her truck, she sped down the bumpy road and headed for the shortcut over the hill. Beth ran to meet her partner as she saw the truck rounding the bend near her home.

"Molly was in a panic," Maggie explained as Beth climbed into the cab. "She was all dressed for a business appointment. There was nothing she could do, anyway. This is my responsibility, not hers. I have no idea what we'll find when we get there. She just told me that Gabriel is torn and bleeding. If he's been attacked by the deer, as she thinks, he could be in bad shape. Those hoofs can be treacherous and inflict real damage."

Once at the ranch and through the gate, they rounded the hill to the five acres containing the captive deer. They parked just inside the fence, then scanned the site quickly—no Gabriel. The other deer vanished quickly into the lower grove. Maggie's eyes followed them down the narrow path. "Which way do we go? Where do we begin to search?" she wondered. Guided by some inner instinct, she decided to take the high trail that led to a small stand of oak. As they searched, Maggie called, "Gabriel! Gabriel, where are you?" They passed over the crest of the hill, glancing in every direction as they advanced. "Walk carefully. We don't want to frighten him, " she warned. "Watch for any slight movement, any unnatural looking object in the grass. Anything that appears to be different might be Gabriel. There is so much territory to cover. If he's down, he'll be difficult to spot."

"I hope he doesn't think that we're the deer coming after him again," Beth worried. "If he has any strength left, he might bolt and run even farther from the truck. What a job it will be to get him down to the gate if we find him up here."

"We'll manage. All I care about right now is finding him alive."

Just then, directly ahead off to the side of the trail, something caught Maggie's eye. "There! What's that dark object to the left? Do you see a slight movement? Look! Beyond that tangle of brush. I think that's him. Careful, don't startle him."

As the two women moved closer, Gabriel lifted his head above the carpet of grass. Gaping open-mouthed, he attempted to rise, but fell back to the ground. "Gabriel, you're alive!" She approached the injured deer cautiously. "Oh, Gabriel, you're alive," she repeated with relief as she knelt to wipe caked, drying blood from above his eyes.

"Oh, Maggie, look at him. He can't even stand. How will we handle him? He's much too big to carry on the stretcher. We can't begin to lift him." Beth walked slowly toward Maggie and Gabriel. "How awful. Those wounds on his back look deep. He must be in pain. He'll need a vet, won't he?"

"No doubt about that," Maggie answered. Her first concern was to get him on his feet and over the hill to the truck. Two small women couldn't handle this large yearling any other way.

Maggie crouched beside him and tried to lift him. Gabriel lay exhausted, hurt and frightened. "Gabriel, you must get up. You must walk. Get up, Gabriel. Help me. We can't do it without your help."

She continued lifting his head, thrusting her arms under his heavy body to encourage him to stand. "Come on, big guy, you can do it. Please, please try."

As if in answer to her pleas, sensing the urgency in her voice, Gabriel stirred haltingly, then rose unsteadily to his feet. Maggie understood his pain as he stood swaying before her. Beth held her breath, hoping he wouldn't sink back onto the ground.

Placing one hand on his neck and the other on his flank, Maggie gently pushed him forward. The dazed yearling staggered down the path by her side. She talked soothingly as she guided him down the trail toward the gate. "That's the boy, one small step at a time. Not much farther, Gabriel, just keep those wobbly legs moving and we'll make it. We're almost there. Good boy, Gabriel. Good boy."

At the foot of the hill, Gabriel stopped to drink from the water trough. He lowered his head weakly to take a small mouthful of grain. "I wonder how long he's been without nourishment? The whole two days?"

"Do you think they attacked him when he first approached their food?" Beth speculated. "They must have considered him an intruder."

As though in answer, the other deer abruptly appeared on the other side of the field, heads down, purposely heading in their direction. "Look, Maggie!" Beth screamed. "Here they come, looking like they mean business."

"No! They mustn't. They must not interfere. We can't handle them and Gabriel, too. We can all be in danger. Here, Beth, stand beside Gabriel so he doesn't fall or try to run. Keep him distracted. Give him a handful of grain and try to lead him to the truck."

Maggie left Gabriel's side and ran toward the threatening trio, waving her arms and shouting loudly to frighten them off. They stopped suddenly, stared at her briefly, then turned and fled back into the safety of the trees.

Beth successfully guided the frightened yearling to the truck. She threw the remaining grain onto the floor of the camper, and as Gabriel struggled toward it, Maggie hoisted his front legs up onto the tailgate, put her shoulder against his rump, and pushed with all the strength she could muster. Beth added a firm lift, and Gabriel willingly cooperated by pulling himself up into the covered bed of the truck.

Maggie closed herself inside the camper to examine him more closely. She determined that his wounds were too serious to treat without the help of a vet. Bleeding abrasions covered most of his head and body. She touched his small antlers that he had so proudly displayed, noting that one was broken at the base, while the tip of the other dangled uselessly. His eyes, surrounded by small cuts, had no detectable injuries.

As she climbed out of the camper, she told Beth, "He obviously needs surgery and medication. The closest vet is Dr. Bailey in Cloverdale, about fifteen miles north. We'll just have to hope he's in and not too busy to treat Gabriel. I don't like to stop in without first calling, but there's no phone."

Maggie carefully navigated the winding back roads out of the hills. Before long they were traveling the straight and easy highway to Cloverdale.

"It looks as though our deer at Molly's have learned their wild ways well," Maggie reflected. "They instinctively defended a territory they claim as their own. The limited space apparently didn't allow room to absorb another nearly full-grown deer. They didn't come into the enclosure together, and although Molly said they cuffed the last arrival to assign her a place in the group, they didn't hurt her as they did Gabriel."

Maggie drove the straight ribbon of highway lost in thought, then continued to voice her concern. "I didn't anticipate this vicious attack. I didn't think there was any reason to worry about him not fitting in. These are not adult wild deer. Maybe the habitat became too crowded, creating an instinctive threat to the three older deer. Maybe Gabriel is too tame, and wasn't prepared to defend himself from the wilder group. What an awful way to learn such an important lesson about deer in captivity. A lesson I won't easily forget."

"Well, they had no way of knowing that Gabriel wouldn't be there for long, or that they would soon be free themselves," reasoned Beth. "Do you ever have a problem of this kind when you put a new arrival in with an established group of fawns?"

"Sometimes there's a slight skirmish. I had one very young male walk right up to each fawn as it came into the pen and smack it on the shoulder," Maggie laughed, as she recalled the incident. "It didn't matter if it were male or female. He was an aggressive little guy. I couldn't help but be impressed. I knew he would be a survivor.

He was definitely in charge for the entire season. They soon settled down and enjoyed being together. I've never had this serious kind of trouble before. Maybe I should have paid better attention to the message that little buck delivered."

Upon arrival at the vet's office, Maggie hurried in to explain the emergency to Dr. Bailey. "I hate to barge in on you, but this buck is in real trouble. Do you have time to take a look at him?"

"My next client isn't due for a few minutes. Let's see what we can do," offered Dr. Bailey, as they headed in the direction of the parking lot.

One quick glance at Gabriel was enough to send Dr. Bailey rushing into the clinic for a tranquilizer. "Can you hold him while I give him this shot, Maggie? I just want to make him manageable enough to get him into the emergency room."

Maggie climbed in with Gabriel to hold him tightly. He leaned weakly against her thigh as Dr. Bailey gave him the injection. While waiting for the medication to take effect, Maggie related the yearling's many adventures to the vet.

"Quite an eventful life for one small deer," he commented, as he watched Gabriel for signs of the drug taking effect. Then, lowering the tailgate, they lifted the submissive deer down onto the driveway. Beth opened doors ahead, as Maggie guided Gabriel, relaxed and slightly dazed, in the front door of the clinic, down the hallway, and into the treatment room. A vet technician spread a blanket on the floor to keep the unsteady deer on his feet during the examination and treatment.

"These wounds look far worse than they are, Maggie. Most of them are superficial. With some medication to control infection, they'll heal nicely. The skin is rubbed raw, which is why there is so much bleeding, but the abrasions aren't deep." Gabriel flinched as the vet gently touched his antlers. "The most serious injury is to these antlers. The left one will have to come off at the base and be cauterized. There's no guarantee how it will grow back, if it grows back at all. The right one has a broken tip. The velvet is shredded, causing it to bleed, too. I'll snip off the tip, and that antler should be fine."

Leaving the office with medication in her hand and gratitude in her heart, Maggie led the complacent Gabriel out to the truck. Beth and Dr. Bailey lifted the very weary, stressed young buck into the camper.

"What a shame that his beautiful horns were damaged so badly. Will they grow back?" asked Beth, as she glanced through the rear window into the camper where the battered young deer lay sleeping.

"Deer have antlers, not horns," Maggie said. She explained that antlers are solid bone. They are discarded each fall and renewed in the spring, in contrast to the horns of a mountain goat or sheep, which are permanent, non-renewable, hollow structures. In the wild, antlers become a valuable part of the food chain, providing nourishment for smaller mammals. They help keep the teeth of the squirrel and rabbit gnawed down to proper length. They provide calcium. There are many good uses for those discarded antlers.

"Now, to answer your question," continued Maggie. "We'll have to wait until spring to know about Gabriel's antlers, when they should grow back. Let's hope the base heals well and wasn't destroyed during the treatment so they will grow normally again."

Upon returning Gabriel to Molly's ranch, Maggie decided to move him into the vacant fawn enclosure on the other side of the hill. It provided a safe habitat where he could recover from his traumatic experience. Out of necessity, he would be alone as he healed and adjusted to a natural wild life. Maggie felt confident that he would be content here. As she and Beth left the pen, Maggie offered him a handful of oak leaves, which he grabbed hungrily and devoured in obvious enjoyment. She knew he would rest, during his many weeks of recovery, under a dense canopy of trees with the soothing sounds of nature surrounding him.

7

The Farmer's Barn

Molly's fawn pen proved to be ideal recovery quarters for the battered yearling. His quiet was undisturbed except for an occasional free roaming sheep that reached through the fence for some scattered grain, or the Steller's Jay that boldly perched on Gabriel's water trough to share a drink.

However, Gabriel's restlessness showed clearly as his strength and health returned. Ready to experience his first venture into a truly natural world, he paced the perimeter of the fenced area ceaselessly, looking beyond his present boundaries and into the dense forest where his destiny lay. His area to explore extended for many more miles than he would ever need to travel. To the west, remote Lake Sonoma provided him with seclusion, a continuous supply of fresh water, and an abundance of nourishing food that grew lushly along its shores. Finally, after a lifetime of confinement, the healthy, eager yearling slowly and contentedly wandered out through the open gate. He journeyed along the age-old paths, randomly sampling new succulent browse retrieved from the low growing brush. A new soft bed of leaves awaited him whenever the urge to nap arose. There were no fences to keep him from indulging his inclination to roam beyond the next range of hills.

Gabriel explored farther each day, still returning each night to the security of the shelter. Always having been captive, his total conversion from captive to wild would be gradual. It was still too soon to know if he could sever his strong relationship with man.

During one of his daily excursions Gabriel turned north to wander along a winding dirt road he had not yet traveled. As he rounded a sharp bend, the road sloped into a wide luxuriant valley. A gusty wind blew up the grade. Wild grasses swayed in the brisk air. His nose picked up a familiar scent. Following in the scent's direction, he moved confidently into a farm yard. A group of horses, munching their early-morning meal of alfalfa, ignored the advancing buck. The occasional sight of a distant deer caused no anxiety among these country-raised horses. However, Gabriel didn't hesitate to close the distance between them. He boldly intruded into the feeding section of the barnyard. As he casually bent to taste the green hay, the horses reared and flailed furiously. They neighed and loudly protested his intrusion, alerting a farmer, who rushed out the barn door to investigate the disturbance. At the sight of the buck, his head half hidden in a bale of hay, the farmer angrily shouted and waved his pitchfork in Gabriel's direction.

The bewildered deer cautiously withdrew out of the farmer's range. He stood by the side of the road peering uncertainly back at the still raging farmer and the horses that had quietly returned to their feeding.

From the beginning of Molly's involvement with Fawn Rescue the neighboring ranchers and farmers had voiced no objection to the facility or its goals. This was the first disturbing incident ever attributed to any wildlife released from her ranch. However, the irate farmer didn't hesitate to call her at once to protest the presence of the uninhibited deer intruding into his barnyard. "Molly, I won't tolerate wildlife creating havoc among my livestock," he said. "These are high-strung show horses. They're of great value. That deer will be shot if he wanders into my barnyard again." He told Molly to wait while he looked out his office window. "Yes, he's still standing out there on the road. If you want to keep him alive, you had better come and remove him, or I will. He won't be given a second chance."

Molly rushed down immediately to escort the wayward deer back home. The uneasy Gabriel followed her willingly up the hilly dirt road as she led the way with an apple in her hand.

Once more Maggie received a frantic call from Molly. "Maggie, what next? I love Gabriel, you know that. But I can't take this constant aggravation. This rancher is my neighbor. I have to respect his rights as a landowner. He'll naturally protect his livestock and he's serious when he vows to shoot Gabriel. You'll have to find another place for him. He's in the fawn pen right now, but I can't keep him there, and I don't dare release him here again. He's bound to cause more trouble. It's just not working."

Maggie agreed. "You're right, of course, Molly. You can't have that disruption. How would we guess that he would wander so far? I was sure your four-hundred acres, and the miles of wilderness beyond, would be enough range for him. How far away did he go to find this barn? I wasn't aware that you had any close neighbors."

"It would be all the range he would ever need if he had gone in any other direction," Molly replied. "Instead, he went down the north side of our property line. I hadn't thought how close we really are to each other at that point. They're settled just at the edge, about a half mile from here."

Maggie hesitated, then said, "I do hate to ask you for one more favor, because you've been pushed to your limit with this experience. But will you please leave Gabriel in the fawn pen and lock the gate? That will keep him out of trouble, and out of danger, until I can find a place for him." She pleaded, "I promise you, it will be soon." Her distraught friend consented to do this.

Maggie turned to Beth in total frustration. "I need a cold drink. I can't think right now. Will I ever find a home for that imprinted deer where he will be safe as well as free?"

"Here, relax. Have some iced tea and tell me the latest bad news." The intern had many questions as she listened. "Maybe this would be a good time to explain to me the difference between imprinting and bonding. I know Gabriel is proving to be a classic case of imprinting. How is that different from bonding? Can either of them be reversed? How serious a problem is this for wildlife to overcome?"

Maggie began by explaining bonding first, how a baby bonds to its mother, as all living creatures do—humans as well as wildlife. A baby needs the nurturing it receives from its mother. These close ties are usually binding, but this bond can be broken. If an infant is removed from its mother it will most likely forget her. However, a baby can bond again. A very young infant will sometimes bond to the next one to care for it, as in adoptions. "In my work with animals," continued Maggie, "I find that a newborn fawn will bond to me as the mother substitute. I feed it, I keep its body clean and provide nurturing. A fawn won't break this bond willingly. So, it's up to me to break it."

"I see, so that's why you're anxious to get it in with another fawn right away."

"Yes, I put them together so they'll relate to their own species rather than to humans. I withdraw all contact, except for the necessary feeding and care."

"But what about an older fawn that has already bonded with its mother?"

"In that case, I never allow it to bond with me. I limit my contact with it. It joins the other fawns and instinctively rejects me. They eat and sleep together, and are released together. After release, they stay as a group, forming their own family nucleus. I've been documenting proof of this over the years."

Maggie continued to explain the difference between bonding and imprinting. "Now, imprinting is harder to deal with." Imprinting, she explained, is the process of impressing behavior and skills upon the mind of a baby. The young one learns the proper methods for survival by imitation and observation. Finding food, shelter, learning to fear predators. When a wild baby is taken out of its natural environment and is raised by humans, as Gabriel was, it loses its fear of humans, becomes dependent upon them, and doesn't develop the skills necessary for survival in the wild. Maggie finished her tea and concluded her lesson. "Imprinting means being exposed to humans and domestic animals to the extent that the baby loses all fear of these predators. Humans are predators, like it or not. This lack of fear, as we are learning from Gabriel, seems to be irreversible. It can be a death sentence to a wild animal or bird. An imprinted deer may walk right up to a hunter without fear. I had an experience where a fawn was raised as a pet, wore a red collar around its neck, and was shot. The people who made a pet of it could not understand their responsibility for its death."

"Then what about Gabriel? Can he ever be free?"

"Gabriel has been taught to prefer his own natural foods, but he hasn't forgotten domestic foods, such as alfalfa. He's learned to adjust to the outdoor elements. However, he hasn't given up his relationship with humans, and he probably never will. If he's to enjoy a natural wild life, he must be settled far away from any human habitat. This is what I must find for him. It's a matter of life and death, as you can see."

Maggie realistically acknowledged that this yearling could never again be trusted to be set free in a location containing houses, barns, livestock, gardens, or human habitat of any kind. The options were few. She refused to give up and have him euthanized. "There must be a solution," she insisted. "Finding it is part of the learning. Having problem wildlife euthanized, or caging them for a lifetime, has always been the easy way out. I want to find a place where he can fit into this mixed up world." She never doubted that one day Gabriel would be free.

Maggie spent the next several days on the phone exploring many possibilities that led to dead ends. One evening she called her long time friend Angie to ask for help. From her work with wildlife Angie knew many people who lived in wilderness areas, and one person came to mind as Maggie presented Gabriel's varied problems. "He lives alone," offered Angie. "A real lover of animals. He has quite a variety living on his property. I know him well. He can be trusted to do what's needed to help Gabriel. His ranch is isolated at the end of Creek Canyon, not too far from you. It should be perfect."

Angie checked with her friend Jake Carter, then called Maggie. "Good news. He said he'd be happy to have Gabriel on his land. Gabriel will have the space and time to adjust at his own speed. There's no one else living within many miles." A safe haven for Gabriel, at last.

The next day Maggie met with Jake and Angie to inspect the property. " I have one small favor to ask of you, Maggie," said Jake, as he grinned broadly through his long, white beard. "I have this one lonesome old sheep, and I'd be willing to make a trade. If you can find a home for this sheep, I mean, a good home where she can be with other sheep and not be butchered, I'll let your buck live here until he gets out on his own."

"Done deal." Maggie's friend Molly had sheep that she treated like pets. "I'm sure I have the perfect place for your lonesome ol' gal. She'll live out her life in luxury," Maggie assured him.

The day before Gabriel's transfer, Maggie released the last group of fawns for the year. As she had done countless times before on these releases, she backed the truck up to the water source, a crucial factor in choosing release sites for the animals. Maggie opened the tail gate, the leader leaped out with a forceful, unhesitating bound, and the others followed immediately. They stopped briefly to drink, then disappeared into the trees with never a backward look. "Look at that," she said to Beth. "That's just as it should be. No 'goodby', no 'thanks a lot,' or 'see you later' from this bunch of wild and eager juveniles. They'll do well, I'm sure." Then she added, "It will be rewarding to have Gabriel settled before the fall rains begin and to have the season end so successfully."

That evening Maggie apprehensively answered the shrill, persistent ring of the phone. A call late in the evening usually meant more wildlife problems. However, she wasn't prepared to hear Angie on the line. "Maggie, I'm so sorry. Jake can't take Gabriel after all."

"Why? What happened?" Maggie felt her pulse leap. Her vision of Gabriel's peaceful retirement vanished. "Did he give you a reason? Is it something we could work out?"

"No. He was firm. I didn't ask why. He said he thought it was best for him this way. I'm sure he has a good reason for the last minute change. I wish I could do something. I feel so bad. I know how important this is to you. What will you tell Molly? What will you do now?"

Even though the news was disappointing, Maggie accepted it with resignation, knowing a better solution would come. It always did. "I'll sleep on it, Angie. Don't blame yourself. These things happen. Thanks for trying."

In the morning Maggie drove north through the fog to pick up Gabriel as planned. She felt that she couldn't retreat from this issue. "He's my responsibility," she told Beth as they traveled. "I'll find a good home for him. I know I will. Molly has been good about helping me over the years, and I gave her my word to get Gabriel off her ranch today. So he's coming with us. None of us could have anticipated this latest setback. We won't mention it to her, okay? I don't want to worry her. I'll tell her about it some day when all this is just a memory—a happy memory."

Molly waited by the gate with two of her employees. "Open the gate and I'll back up against it," instructed Maggie. Then the group lined up on either side of Gabriel. On the count of 'three,' they hoisted him up into the camper. Maggie closed the hatch, waved goodby, and without a second thought, drove directly home to Fawn Rescue. Because of yesterday's releases, the pens were empty now. Gabriel would be at home where he belonged until she found the ideal spot—that perfect home, that illusive sanctuary—for this extraordinary young deer.

8

At Fawn Rescue

A dense network of branches filtered the deepening shadows over Gabriel's new dwelling at Fawn Rescue. Saucy squirrels scurried nimbly down the trunks of the oaks, aggressively demanding their quota of acorns and grain, then quickly retreated to a high limb far overhead to devour their prize. Wary foxes, timid hares, and quail foraged at Gabriel's feed trays. As the sun faded, a crow's shrill caw pierced the evening air, as though orchestrating the busy diners from his vantage point above. Nocturnal raccoons peered guardedly from behind furry masks as they approached to grope for the smallest portion of food remaining after sundown. The chirps, chatter, growls and trills of these wild creatures became familiar background notes for the young deer.

Daily Gabriel watched the resident wild deer travel the trails of their ancestors as they climbed up from the creek and veered sharply to walk in single file along the fence enclosing him. The lonely yearling stood beyond the barrier, unmoving, following them with his eyes.

Fall arrived early, bursting with colorful leaves. High in the fir trees, eager gray squirrels ripped nut-filled cones from the swaying tips of the branches. Empty cone flakes dropped steadily, forming into piles of cone shavings around the floor of the pen, providing a soft bed for the young buck.

Gabriel's body adjusted naturally to the dry fall menu and cooler temperatures. His coat thickened, sleek and glistening, turning slowly to a dark wintery gray. As he grew, his appetite for natural foods increased. Maggie's neighbor provided baskets of luscious apples that loosened their grip daily and dropped to the ground as they ripened. Gabriel stripped the hanging branches of their meager foliage. He rubbed his short stunted antlers against the tree trunks, tearing loose the bark, causing damage to the fresh new growth. Because of his mature growth, Gabriel could not remain much longer within the confines of Fawn Rescue's limited boundaries.

Each new day found Maggie gathering acorns, fresh leaves and vines to supplement the limited supply within the yearling's confines. She became a familiar figure following the tree trimmers as they worked along the highways and back roads.

She parked her small white truck alongside the enormous road equipment, as the trimmers sheared the overhanging growth and pushed the branches into piles for pulverizing and cleanup. Maggie then worked from the piles, clipping quickly and tossing the leaves into the back of the camper. The trimmers liked the idea of contributing something so valuable to Fawn Rescue, something that would have otherwise been discarded. The road crews knew her by name and looked forward to her daily visits.

"How much longer will you be here today?" she asked one morning, as she pulled alongside the workmen.

"Need leaves for those starving fawns, Maggie?" they laughed and motioned for her to pull off the road.

"It's not for young fawns this time, guys. No more fawns until next spring. But I've got a yearling buck that will eat all the greens you can give me," she said.

"We can spare a truckload or two. They're all yours. Take your time. We'll probably be here most of the day."

"Great. I'm on a call from Glen Ellen, but should be back within an hour. This is such a help, especially in the summer when I have dozens of hungry mouths to feed and have a hard time finding enough to satisfy them. You get the branches up high where I can't reach. I'll see you in about an hour, then." Maggie waved and headed south toward Glen Ellen.

Through years of random picking and testing, Maggie learned that poison oak was a favorite food of the fawns—the first choice selected from any variety of vegetation offered to them. Now, after carefully donning protective clothing and gloves, Maggie picked baskets full for Gabriel. He grabbed greedily as she tossed the delicacies over the high fence into his pen.

Gabriel settled into his home at Fawn Rescue, content with his new surroundings. He greeted Maggie eagerly each time she entered the gate. She ran ahead of him through the pen to encourage him to exercise and practice his stiff four-legged stot. This vertical leap, unique to his species, permits unpredictable changes of direction in mid air, and a landing with all four hoofs touching the earth at one time. This tactic enables the deer to foil a predator's calculations and escape from its lunge. Maggie knew that Gabriel's body must develop strength and agility to prepare him for his eventual freedom. Fleetness, alertness, awareness, and knowledge of things natural to his habitat were essential skills he would need for survival in the wild.

Gabriel's hoofs had grown long in captivity. The hoofs, teeth and claws of various animals continue to grow throughout their lifetime. Nature helps keep them trim in the wild by the constant climbing, gnawing, and running that the animal must do. To correct Gabriel's problem, Maggie called a large-animal veterinarian, Dr. Adams, asking him to restore the hoofs to their proper length. This was an unusual request for him, but he was intrigued with the prospect of working with a full-grown buck. Therefore, he arranged to visit Fawn Rescue the following day.

Dr. Adams drove up the winding dirt road to Fawn Rescue and parked near the wood-paneled chute into which the fawns were driven when they were captured for treatment or release. His well-stocked van included various clippers and rasps, medications, and gloves. After meeting his new patient, the doctor arranged his equipment and filled a syringe. As he worked, he explained the procedure to Maggie. “I'm giving him a very light dose of a tranquilizer,” he said. “Deer are extremely sensitive to drugs. Even a slight overdose can kill one.” He estimated the weight of the uneasy yearling that waited in the confinement of the chute. “I don't want to put him out. This diluted dose will make him manageable without causing him harm.”

Beth photographed the event. As Maggie and Dr. Adams entered the chute, Beth said, “I'll try to get some good photos for our records. I can't imagine this ever happening again.”

“Let's hope not,” laughed Maggie.

The carefully measured amount of tranquilizer soon put Gabriel into a submissive mood. He yielded his hoof as the vet lifted, clipped, and filed each one in turn. Maggie held Gabriel to comfort him during the process. After forty-five minutes, the stressed buck had reached his limit of endurance and began to resist. "Let him lie down, Maggie. I can finish this last hoof easily from here." Maggie released her hold and the young deer's heavy body sagged slowly to the ground. "We're almost through, big guy," said Dr. Adams, "then you can rest for as long as you like."

Packing to leave, Dr. Adams said, "Call me anytime you aren't able to get one of your charges to your regular vet. I'm out in the field most of the time and I can always stop by in an emergency."

Maggie thanked him and promised to mail a photo of the event to mount on the bulletin board at his clinic.

Gabriel's new trim enabled him to enjoy exercising more. He ran and stotted, playfully leaped and flipped like a young fawn, belying his growing size and strength. Gabriel made great strides in readying himself for his survival in the wild. Watching his progress proved to be a delightful experience for Maggie.

Some days were more challenging than others. One misty morning new neighbors permitted their young Husky to run free to exercise. It eventually found its way to Gabriel's pen. The scent of the wild deer inflamed the dog as it circled and chased wildly around the enclosure. It barked and yelped in a frenzy. It charged and snarled, raged and taunted. Gabriel reacted violently to the threat. He leaped and threw himself against the sturdy high fence in an attempt to escape the fierce attack. He raced up and down the pen frantically, bounding from side to side in panic.

Hearing the commotion, realizing the insane barking was coming from the direction of the pen, Maggie dashed to Gabriel's aid, screaming as she ran, "No! Get away! Go home!" She grabbed a broken branch off the ground and, in a fury, threw it in the direction of the excited dog. Immediately he dropped his vicious attitude and turned to disappear into the trees, racing toward home.

Maggie entered the enclosure to find Gabriel standing near collapse under his shelter. Head thrown back, he gasped for air, while small drops of foam formed on either side of his gaping mouth. In this dazed, shocked condition, he folded himself to the ground as Maggie approached. Gently she examined his wounds. A large patch of hair, torn from his left shoulder still clung to the fence. The velvet from his one twisted antler hung loose and bloody. His nose and forehead were covered with abrasions caused by the force of his blows against the fence. Maggie wiped his head with cool damp towels and dressed his wounds, calming and reassuring him as she worked. She stayed close by his side until he finally rested comfortably.

Leaving Gabriel to recover from the trauma, Maggie visited her neighbors who owned the dog. She explained her work and emphasized the lovely countryside filled with vulnerable wildlife. She reminded them of the county ordinance against allowing dogs to run uncontrolled. "These laws are essential to the welfare of defenseless wildlife whose lives are always at risk," she said.

Taking a defensive stance, the Albertsons claimed to have never had any reason to imagine Bruin would harm anything wild or domestic. They admitted that it was true that he had never been free to run until now. He had always been confined to a large yard, therefore, this experience was new to him. "One of the reasons we loved moving to the country was so he could have the fun of roaming free," said Mr. Albertson. "He's such a sweet dog." Bruin sat pressing into Mr. Albertson's thigh, looking up into his face, gentle and innocent.

Maggie smiled and carefully explained, "Yes, we had to learn new rules for our pets when we moved from Southern California. The living is different here. Now we are intensely protective of wildlife, a privilege we never dreamed of before we moved north."

"But Bruin is so loving. He simply can't be considered dangerous," protested Mrs. Albertson, looking fondly across the room at the Husky. As if on cue, the dog thumped his tail softly on the carpet in response.

"Even the most loving pet can become dangerous when aroused by a strange wild scent, or by catching the quick furtive movement of a creature fleeing through the brush. Dogs that are released for a few hours of exercise after dark can group into packs and incite each other into acts not otherwise expected of a gentle family companion. Each of us must take responsibility for our own pets." To strengthen her point, Maggie added, "Another thing to keep in mind, Mr. Albertson. In this county, Bruin will be shot by a rancher if he attempts to terrorize livestock the way he did this wild deer."

"Yes, I can see what you're saying. Looks as though we've moved back into a remaining bit of the wild west. Well, Bruin won't give you any more difficulty. I think he will be much safer confined to our three acres, which will certainly provide him with all the room he needs to run."

After the dog attack, Gabriel became extremely sensitive to sudden movement and unusual sounds. He now exhibited a legitimate fear of dogs. His nervousness gradually subsided into an alertness that would serve him well in the future.

As the days shortened and fall eased into winter, the floor of Gabriel's pen became pulverized from his constant activity. Paths became ruts. Wet weather turned earth into mud. The early winter rains offered the growing buck a special delight. He splashed through the downpour as the cool water ran off his impenetrable, sleek coat. He lay on a fragrant bed of pine needles under a towering fir tree, returning to his dry shelter only at night where he slept with the sound of the driving rain pelting on the rooftop. Gabriel spent a peaceful and safe winter at Fawn Rescue.

The rapidly approaching spring would bring new challenges for Gabriel and his care giver. The enclosure he now called home soon would be filled with young fawns and needed to be restored to accommodate the new arrivals. Maggie never lost sight of Gabriel's need for a natural habitat, one with abundant space and ample food and water. Her search for Gabriel's permanent home became urgent.

9

A New Beginning

Over the years, throughout the northwest, Elaine Harper had purchased several large parcels of undeveloped land through her family foundation. The foundation, legacy of her parents, then claimed these wilderness parcels for wildlife. As she administered the foundation, Elaine found it increasingly more difficult to find true, unspoiled wilderness that would be suitable for wildlife preserves. The unchecked spread of civilization reached into too many wilderness regions. Her latest quest for acreage in the Northern California region proved to be frustrating for her. Then suddenly, she found the perfect parcel that suited her every requirement. "I had begun to think I'd never find anything to satisfy me," she said one blustery spring afternoon, while informing Maggie of her purchase. "I swear, my whole life has been dedicated to researching, but it has been time well spent. Just wait until you see what I've found." She asked Maggie to join her for a day of touring her new two-thousand-acre preserve. "Wear your boots," she warned. "We've had a lot of rain up there, and it's pretty mucky. I'll pick you up early."

At dawn the two friends piled binoculars, thermoses, jackets, and other travel necessities into Elaine's sturdy van. The three-hour drive allowed plenty of time for Elaine to outline the long-range goals of the foundation. "Our focus is to add to the inventory of wildlands. Too much natural habitat has already disappeared. Now that we've made our choice, there is so much to do. It's hard to put any of it aside, but we've already decided that our first project will be the removal of every foot of barbed wire that crisscrosses and surrounds the land. We just can't live with it."

Maggie approved. "You can't believe how many fawns and adult deer I find either helplessly hanging or entangled in barbed wire. They're mangled beyond help. That treacherous fencing is archaic. There are other types of fencing that keep livestock in and wildlife out, if that's the reason for its installation."

"That's why it's coming down," continued Elaine."Then, once the land is safe again, our next priority will be to build a cabin for our manager, Brad Spencer. For now, he's living in a mobile home on the property. He loves it up there. No phones. No electricity. Real rugged living. He'll be the only human within many miles. The surrounding pieces of land are just as wild as ours. We eventually hope to open the refuge to wildlife research groups. Brad has a wildlife management degree. We're lucky to have found a person so qualified to fit our needs. He understands our goals, and he'll be there to guard the property from poachers and other intruders."

Maggie loved what she was hearing and congratulated Elaine on her good fortune in finding the site. "But there's more," said Elaine. "We hope you will consider using the refuge as a release site for Fawn Rescue."

"The perfect answer to my dilemma."

"What dilemma?"

As they drove, Maggie unfolded Gabriel's saga, crisis after crisis. The hours and miles sped by for the two women as they discussed Gabriel's needs and his serious handicaps. Maggie listed the requirements that must be met to establish a safe haven for Gabriel and for any other fawns that might need special protection in the future.

"I make an extensive tour of any land before using it as a release site," Maggie explained. "It has to be just right. I don't simply take them to the nearest park and dump them. It must be located far away from public roads or highways. It would make no sense to have them killed within days after they were set free. A year-round water source, and an abundance of natural browse are essential. There's still more," she laughed at her long list of requirements that seemed to be unending. "A perimeter of many miles of no hunting is something I check out carefully. I once found a great spot, only to learn, just in time, that there was a hunting club about a mile away. Last, but most crucial for Gabriel, as we have learned, there must be no human habitat."

"Well, you can't put months of effort into raising fawns only to release them in a disastrous location," Elaine agreed.

"So, what do you think?" Maggie asked her friend. "Do you still feel as enthusiastic about your generous offer? May I bring Gabriel to live out his life in your wildlife sanctuary? He'll still be my responsibility, of course. I'd remove him at once, just as I've had to do before, if he were to cause any trouble for you."

Elaine pondered for a brief moment before asking, "I'm wondering about his being neutered, Maggie. How will that affect him in the wild?"

"It shouldn't matter. I've checked through all my reference books on deer. Neutering can happen accidentally in the wild. A stag is a neutered buck. They're able to function normally, except for mating, of course."

Elaine hesitated no longer. "I'm sure that if Gabriel is ever going to find a safe haven anywhere, it will be on our preserve. Bring him up. Brad lives on a very small section. All the rest is totally natural. Brad will respect the yearling's wildness and his right to be free without any interference."

As they approached the small town of Willits, Elaine pulled into the market to purchase groceries for lunch. "Brad never has anything stocked for guests," explained Elaine. "There's nothing beyond Willits and we still have close to fifteen miles to drive. I'd better fill up with gas, too. I'm in no mood to hike out."

In a short while Elaine pulled the van onto a winding five-mile dirt road that led over low-lying hills toward the wooded highlands. As the van climbed, and the terrain turned more rugged, Elaine announced that they had crossed the border into her property. Maggie glanced through her open window to view the pristine woodlands and breathe the fresh scent of cool forest air, still damp from recent spring rains. She smiled as they passed the deep, rambling river marking the eastern border of this two-thousand-acre preserve. She noted the natural springs, ponds, and rushing streams, the abundant vegetation, and the ample cover of brush, all components on her list of necessities. The deep forest, the towering fir and the massive-limbed oaks gave way to vistas of open meadows dotted with golden California poppies. As they drove into the core of the mountain, she thought, breathtaking beauty, yes, but equally bountiful as a refuge where nature thrives in its purest form. Finally, the search for Gabriel's home had come to an end.

"What an ideal spot for my wayward buck. No livestock to harass, no gardens to raid, no barns, vineyards, grainfields . . . " Maggie declared. "This is so perfect . . . " She continued to soak up the magnificence of the forest and meadows. "...a natural, safe environment. No interference from man. What a dream."

"He'll have his five miles of roaming space," said Elaine.

"At last. The animal gods have had their hand in this one, don't you think?"

Elaine nodded, then said, "I'm pleased that we can make it available to him."

"After all that he's been through, he's finally healthy and eager to be free." Maggie ran down her checklist. "His body has been exposed to all the weather conditions he will encounter in the wild. He prefers his natural foods, he displays a fear of dogs, and reacts instantly to any unusual disturbance. Only his trust of man remains as the one dangerous barrier that he hasn't yet overcome. And I don't think that will be a problem here."

Brad met Elaine and Maggie beside the van as they pulled up to the mobile home. He welcomed the prospect of having Gabriel as the first release of wildlife on the refuge. "He'll fit right in with all the other wild creatures here. We have a small herd of resident deer that appear every evening at the crest of that mountain above us and migrate down through the canyon to the left." He pointed to the impressive mountain behind the building site. Maggie visualized the peaceful scene as he spoke. "This territory is certainly vast enough to absorb additional wildlife. Even with the larger mammals we see now and then, such as bear, coyote, mountain lion, elk, and the smaller bobcats, Gabriel should find his own space here. However," he added, "we have to be realistic and acknowledge that all wildlife is at risk throughout their lifetime. There are no guarantees in nature, are there?"

"Even so," Maggie said, "Gabriel deserves his chance. He can't spend any more of his life in confinement. This sure beats living at Animal World."

Brad, Elaine and Maggie walked through the brush and over a ravine to decide upon a location for Gabriel's temporary pen. They chose a perfect spot for a spacious enclosure to extend around a thick stand of oak and underbrush. It would serve as his home until he became adjusted. In the future, other fawns would be released from this sturdy pen, as well.

Maggie knew that Gabriel must be moved to his new home quickly. Fawns would arrive within a few short weeks, and she needed time to restore the fawn facility. "That big guy has torn up the large pen so badly. It will take a lot of work to repair it. How lucky I am that you can get his space ready so soon, Brad."

They made plans for Gabriel's transfer.

*

At the close of a wildlife meeting the following week, Maggie told the Department of Fish and Game Patrol Warden Alan Manning that she had found a perfect spot for the yearling at last. "Since he'll be moving north into Mendicino County, I'll need your permission for the transfer."

"He's in your care, Maggie. You're the one who knows his needs. Do what you think is best. Let me know how it works out."

They discussed the upcoming fawn season. "You'll be hearing a lot from me. As you know, there always seem to be a few 'pet' fawns you have to confiscate." As they headed toward the exit, Maggie added, "I'm hoping for a better season this year. Last year was hectic—ninety-seven fawns and drought conditions to deal with as well." Maggie waved as she backed out of the parking area. "Think rain, Alan!" And rain it did.

*

It rained steadily the night before Gabriel's transfer. Thick, spongy mud oozed under Gabriel's hoofs as he ran to greet

Maggie at the gate on that cold, drizzly spring morning, his last at Fawn Rescue. The sky was a bleak slate gray. By night a lustrous full moon would illuminate his permanent home.

"One final trip, Gabriel. No more rides, no more adjustments. From now on, it will be just you and deer wonderland," Maggie promised him.

His growing antlers barely cleared the top of the camper shell as Gabriel stood tall and ready for his last journey. Born two years ago, the one-hundred-sixty-five pound robust, muscular buck filled the space well. He watched through the window to see the excited group of wildlife volunteers forming a small caravan behind him. All eight of them would be needed to encircle him on his short passage between the camper and his new pen, allowing him no avenue of escape.

Gabriel's powerful body swayed as the truck rocked and lurched its way down the two miles of rutted dirt road from Fawn Rescue to the highway. He stood alertly gazing out the back window as they came to a halt at a traffic signal in town, causing quite a sensation among the passing motorists who pointed and waved. They rolled down their windows to yell at Maggie. One child screamed over the clamor of the traffic, "Is that a real deer, lady?" Maggie waved and drove on. "Lie down, Gabriel," she pleaded. She wanted this transit to be low key. She had no painted emblem or phone number on her truck to hint at the cargo she often transported through the center of town. She kept her mission quiet, as she carried injured animals to the vet, or transported a group of high-strung juveniles to their new home in the wild. Threats and challenging remarks had made her wary of exposing the fawns to public view.

They traveled at a faster pace once they reached the state highway. Gabriel lay comfortably on the carpeted floor during the three-hour trip north.

Rain intermittently accompanied the group as they sped toward the wildlife refuge. The temperature dropped noticeably when they turned into the thick forest and worked their way back to Brad's hermitage. Deep ruts of thick, slippery mud prevented the truck from climbing the last steep grade to the newly-erected shelter. Brad and Elaine greeted the group from the doorway of the partially-built living quarters. "Typical March weather, gang. We couldn't have chosen a messier time of the year to try this project." Brad pulled his parka over his head while walking toward the truck. "Lucky we have a tractor. We couldn't negotiate this hill without it, and I sure wouldn't want to be in charge of leading that anxious buck in the right direction with all this open space to tempt him."

Brad quickly chained the truck to the muddy tractor. The entire wildlife group floundered up the wet grassy incline beside the truck, laughing as they stumbled and slid in every direction, instantly covering their boots and jeans with mud. The small truck slowly followed in the wake of the tractor and gradually halted as close to the shelter as Brad could safely maneuver it. Gabriel swayed uneasily in the back.

"All right, boys and girls!" shouted Brad. "Let's get together and pay attention. We'll form two lines, one on either side of the big guy. Maggie will lead him into the pen with that big red apple. Hope he's hungry this morning," he joked.

Working together as a well-rehearsed team, they formed a tight passage leading toward the entry gate, making a human chute. Brad let down the tailgate. Gabriel hesitated for an instant, then leaped. His powerful legs served him well as he landed firmly on the spongy, slick grass. "Close in everyone! Tight!" shouted Brad. The group formed a barrier of five on either side, and Gabriel headed straight toward the gate, following the apple that Maggie held enticingly under his nose. Although his two-legged escorts had difficulty keeping their balance, they all finally negotiated the hill, and triumphantly reached their destination. Gabriel willingly followed Maggie through the open gate.

Once inside the enclosure, Gabriel drank deeply from the trough, then began an exploratory tour around his new home. He poked his head into every small crevice under the low hanging brush. He sampled the dark, sharp leaves hanging within his reach. He nibbled the fresh, moist new vegetation spreading thickly across the floor of this hillside haven. As he lifted his head high to inhale the brisk invigorating country air, his eyes wandered beyond the barrier that enclosed him to gaze at the great, cloud-tipped mountain rising solidly into the somber gray sky. He viewed the nearby fields abundant with clusters of thick inviting brush and massive stands of oak. His glance descended into the glen where one day he would gaze at his reflection in eddies along the banks of the tumbling stream as he tasted its pure frigid water. Gabriel was at last in a habitat that was natural to his species. He had found a perfect home.

Maggie estimated that he should be ready to leave the enclosure in three weeks. "I don't want to keep him confined any longer than necessary," she explained to Brad. "He'll have adjusted to his new location by then." Hating to leave, but knowing she must, Maggie headed down the muddy hill for home with the caravan moving in behind her.

The maturing buck adjusted quickly to his new environment and wearied of his limited boundaries. Distant vistas beckoned. He peered restlessly through the restraining fence. He stood impatiently by the gate, as if aware that this was his exit from captivity and his entrance to freedom.

On the final morning of Gabriel's captivity, Maggie arrived early. She felt as anxious for his freedom as he was. A glowing sunrise promised a lustrous, shining day. Gabriel watched Maggie hurry up the slope to his side. The firm bond that had developed between them from their many months of close association had not diminished. Only this once Maggie allowed herself the luxury of showing her deep love for the young buck, an indulgence she never permitted herself with any fawn in her care. They come to her wild and must remain wild. In this one unusual case, it was apparent from the beginning that Gabriel was imprinted with a trust for humans that would remain a permanent part of his nature.

Now, Maggie knew this delightful unique experience must come to an end. This chance occurrence that could never be duplicated must be put behind her. One lesson remained to be learned—one untested concept. Given unlimited freedom, could Gabriel adjust to a natural life? Would he reject his attachment with man and return to his wild origin? A positive, compelling hope gave Maggie the courage to step into the pen where he waited.

A cold, invigorating wind blew sharply down from the mountain peak. Gabriel stood impatiently by the gate as Maggie bid him a tender, emotional farewell. She was filled with optimism and confidence which was tempered with a degree of concern for this experiment, as yet untried.

Maggie opened the gate, and without a departing glance, Gabriel bounded through. Down into the meadow he ran, jubilantly circling through the tall moist grass, stirring up a startled hare that darted swiftly out of his path. Leaping over logs and shrubbery, he displayed an undoubted awareness of his freedom. Making one last rotation, as if in farewell, Gabriel dashed swiftly past the spot where Maggie stood, as tears of joy flowed down her cheeks. Flawlessly he stotted, with magnificent leaps, across a wide trench and up the mountainside. As he disappeared into the distant forest, Maggie softly whispered, "Go safely, my friend. You are free. Goodby, Deer Gabriel, dear, dear Gabriel."

Afterward

During his first few days of freedom, Gabriel returned to sample a few bites of apple or a mouthful of grain. Occasionally Brad observed him lying contentedly in the shelter. His visits became less frequent as weeks passed.

After a lengthy period, Brad caught a glimpse of him browsing in a nearby field, preoccupied and unaware of the manager's close scrutiny. His small twisted antlers caught the rays of the early morning sun. Being certain Gabriel had adjusted well to his new challenge, Brad relaxed his vigil.

Gabriel had broken his bond, and man no longer served a purpose in his life as a wild deer.

Part 2

Wildlife Rescue

Part 2 Prelude
A Commitment to Wildlife

At the sound of the ringing phone everything is put on hold; previous appointments, guests, partially cooked meals, and even sleep. It would seem that wildlife has taken over my life, my home, my family, my every waking hour. This twenty-four hour commitment has a life of its own and is completely out of control.

This commitment involves being available at any time of day or night. I jump into my clothes, then into my Fawnmobile, and race to the scene. Sounds dramatic? It always is. I may be greeted by a tiny four-pound fawn that should never have been removed from its resting spot, one near death that has been brought down by an unattended dog, or possibly a squirrel with a broken leg. The injured animal is rushed to a vet where it is examined and treated. I continue any necessary treatment after bringing it home to a secluded, natural outdoor shelter. These wild creatures, whether well or ill, are fed a formula the equivalent of the mother's milk, plus natural greens that are gathered daily by hand. It's essential to their wildness that they retain their natural fear of man and domestic animals, therefore they must be kept isolated from the public. Once they are fully weaned and able to fend for themselves, they are released far away from humanity on private land.

When I became involved in the care of wildlife the need was evident. There were far too few people with the time or desire to take on such an enormous task. At first I cared for a large variety of mammals, but because of the skills, time and energy required, I found it impossible to do it all and also do it well. My interest led me to specialize in Black-tailed fawns and Western Gray squirrels. I requested a permit from the California Department of Fish and Game and am now operating the only specialized fawn facility in the state of California. Fawns come to me from a vast area.

Through many grass-roots fund raisers I purchased my Fawnmobile — named one day in fun, the name seemed to belong and stayed. This vehicle provides safe and comfortable transportation for the animals.

Wildlife care givers continually search for any means to increase their knowledge of the species they have chosen to rehabilitate. To share my knowledge with other wildlife rehabilitators, I wrote and published two wildlife care manuals, "Black-tailed Fawns, Care in Captivity" and "Western Gray Squirrels, Care in Captivity." These manuals are used by wildlife facilities throughout the United States, Canada, and abroad.

As director of Wildlife Fawn Rescue, I was honored by the California Department of Fish and Game Director's Achievement award for outstanding support of wildlife protection and conservation, and a Statement of Appreciation from the Wildlife Investigations Laboratory of the Department of Fish and Game for pioneering techniques in caring for, and rehabilitation of, fawns.

My rewards far outweigh the effort put into this volunteer work. To watch the slow recovery of an ill or injured young creature, to enjoy observing the steady growth of a wild baby, to witness fawns bounding joyfully across a field to freedom, or squirrels flying from branch to branch high in the tree tops, make my life worthwhile.

M.D.

1
First Fawn

Years of living in the hills above the lovely Valley of the Moon brought me into contact with many injured and orphaned animals, both domestic and wild. Before I became officially involved in wildlife rescue I wasn't aware of the law which requires a permit to possess wildlife for even temporary care. I picked up hares hit by cars, accepted opossums retrieved from garbage cans, received birds with injured wings, and even enjoyed raising one small fawn, Georgie Girl, brought to me by a neighbor who found her lying cold by their pool.

Finally, in my early sixties, I joined a local wildlife organization as a volunteer. I attended my first wildlife meeting with enthusiasm, listing on my application a desire to work with fawns. To prove myself a serious volunteer I went to the required orientation meetings and training classes. I attended monthly meetings, participated in fund raisers, and gradually began to care for small mammals: squirrels, hares, raccoons, foxes. I learned that no one rehabilitated fawns, and under the current policy they were transferred to other counties, or were euthanized.

As spring approached I reminded the director of my interest in caring for fawns. I invited her to visit our home to see how perfectly the land would adapt to building a proper fawn enclosure, and offered to build it at my expense. The property has woodlands, total seclusion, and all the prerequisites for a fawn facility. Each time I brought up the issue, the director avoided giving me a direct answer. Perhaps she felt I couldn't handle such a large, strong animal. Although I enjoyed learning to care for the small mammals that were assigned to me, I still longed to work with fawns.

In addition to animal care, I answered incoming wildlife emergency calls twice a week. One early spring morning, during my phone shift, a concerned young man called seeking help for a fawn. I listened to his report with interest. "Please don't ask my name," he began anxiously. "These are my neighbors, and I hesitate to stir up trouble. However, I know if I don't act today, this fawn will die. It's that urgent."

"There's no need for me to know your name," I assured him. "Tell me about the fawn."

"I've watched it for days. This animal is staked out in the vineyard. There's no shade. It's being fed dry skim milk mixed with water. That's all. There's no nourishment in skim milk, is there? This fawn is so thin and dehydrated, and it cries all the time. It has diarrhea. It's rear is caked and raw." His voice broke as he struggled for composure. "I can't stand it any longer. The fawn is dying. It needs help. I just hope I'm calling the right place."

"You are. But first, have you tried talking to the people who are keeping it tied? Can't they see that it's dying?" I asked.

"I've approached the man who feeds it, several times. He speaks only Spanish. My Spanish isn't too good," the nervous young man continued. "He insists the fawn is fine. No one can take it away from him. He becomes angry when I try to discuss it with him. The man lives alone in one corner of the barn, and the fawn sleeps in there with him at night. During the day he stakes it out close to where he works in the vineyards. No one can get near the little animal. He's very possessive of it."

"Tell me where the fawn is and I'll call in a report right now. I promise you I'll get it today, one way or another," I vowed.

"If you don't, it will be dead. It can't wait another day. I can't stand to hear it cry," he finished in a strained voice.

"Give me your number and I'll get back to you," I said.

"No. I'll keep calling you, if you don't mind," he insisted.

"Call as often as you like. I hope to have good news for you soon. I wish I could just go in and pick up that little captive, but I can't. It's on private property."

"The man is very attached to the fawn and won't give it up easily. It's his pet," he warned. "I thought you might know who to contact for help."

With the phone still in my hand I dialed our wildlife director. Her message machine said she would be gone for the week. Next I called her assistant and learned that she had left for the weekend. Okay, I thought, I'm on my own. Who shall I try next? The Department of Fish and Game? Of course. Simple. They'll confiscate the fawn and all will be well. I had no better luck there. The Department is closed on weekends and I had no emergency number in my file.

Hours passed as I responded to other wildlife calls that required immediate attention. Baby birds fell out of nests. Hares, caught by cats, needed to be picked up for treatment. Volunteers proved to be scarce on weekends. I glanced out the window at the sun gleaming in a cloudless sky and envisioned the small fawn staked to a post and crying.

Between my regular calls I continued my search for help for the fawn. The Humane Society should be open today, I remembered. They'll help, I know. Their operator answered and listened patiently to my request. "This is not what we do," she informed me. "We don't handle wildlife. We're not permitted to bring a wild animal into our facility. Try Animal Control." She gave me the number.

Animal Control's recording instructed me to call the Sheriff's Department for weekend emergencies. I dialed again. This time a real person answered the phone. "Sheriff's

Department. This is Officer Tennor," he said. Relieved, I explained the emergency. "It will still be there on Monday when the Department of Fish and Game can handle it. The fawn isn't going to run off," the officer responded.

"No, the fawn won't be there on Monday. It will be dead. This can't wait," I pleaded.

"You'll have to risk it. We don't handle wildlife emergencies. Sorry, I have another call coming in," the busy officer replied and hung up.

Desperate by then, I phoned other volunteers. None of them knew how this problem should be resolved. "I'm glad I'm not on call for this one," said one. "Baby birds I can handle." I continued to call in to the assistant director's machine, hoping she would pick up the messages I had left.

The day passed as I paced, made more calls, and worried. Finally free of my phone duty, I could now devote full time to finding someone to rescue the fawn. Then I remembered John Sessions, a night driver for the Humane Society—a sensitive man noted for his dedication to animals. Maybe he could advise me, or steer me in another direction. Darkness began to set in. I had so little time left.

Once more I phoned the Humane Society operator. "Jenny, if John's on duty tonight can you put me through to him on his radio phone?" I asked her, not willing to give up hope.

"Yes, he's on duty. Who shall I say is on the line? Is this an emergency?" she asked.

"Yes, Jenny, it is an emergency call," I responded. "Tell him it's Maggie McKenzie. He'll know who I am."

John came through at once. "Hi, Maggie, what's the problem?"

I poured out the details of my day and decided to ask him for his personal help.

"Maggie, you know this isn't what we do."

"I know, John, but if you won't help me, who will?" I pleaded in desperation. "I'll tell you one thing, I'm going to Windsor after that fawn. I'm not going to let it die without making some attempt to save it. We're people who are supposed to care, aren't we? Isn't caring also part of our job?"

"Maggie, you can't go up there alone. It's dangerous, and it's illegal."

"Tell that to the fawn. I'm going, John. I've exhausted all avenues and tried all the correct ways. Now I'll do it my way. I'll be able to convince the man to give the fawn to me. I know I will."

"Wait. I'll try to handle it another way," John said. "I'll call the Sheriff's Department and ask if they'll send a Spanish speaking officer to go up there with me. If we need you we'll meet you there. Give me your number. I'll let you know one way or the other."

John called back within minutes. "Maggie, give me the address of the vineyard. An officer will meet me at the gate. We're going in after that little critter."

"Thank you, John." With a catch in my voice, it was all I could manage to say. I settled in close by the phone to wait. I tried to concentrate on bringing the animal records up to date. Keep busy, I thought, as I reached for my pen.

All day the nameless young man had pressed me for information. When he called again I gave him the latest news. "You finally found help? This is great. I'll be able to see them when they arrive and watch the rescue from my window. Thanks for staying with it," he said gratefully. "I didn't know what to do."

"Neither did I. I'm new at this, too. We just got lucky."

Darkness settled in. I continued my vigil by the phone. Giving in to exhaustion I laid my head on the desk waiting for that magic ring. When it came, I grabbed the phone instantly. "This is Maggie," I said.

"This is Humane Society dispatch. I have a message for you from John."

"Yes?"

"He said, 'Tell Maggie I'll meet her in front of the Kenwood Fire Department at eleven o'clock with the fawn.'" I cried with relief and gratitude.

A few minutes before eleven, John pulled his truck to a stop where I sat waiting. He reached into the back to pull out a tiny, thin, smelly six-pound male. He placed him in my arms with a proud smile.

"Oh, John, you saved this little buck's life. How can I thank you? No other person in the county seemed to be able to help."

"Just take good care of him, Maggie. That's thanks enough."

"Was he difficult to get? Did you have any trouble?" I asked out of curiosity.

"None at all. We got there after dark, as you know. We walked up to the barn and found the man with the fawn. As easy as that. The officer explained the law to him in Spanish and he handed it right over to us without an argument. He admitted to the officer that he knew he had a sick fawn, but he didn't think it would die. Look at him, Maggie. There's no doubt he's a very sick little animal. He wouldn't have lived much longer."

"He'll make it now. He has to," I promised.

Once home, I washed, fed, and settled the tiny buck in a warm bed for the night. The next morning he ran toward the bottle to drink with vigor. I carried him out to place him in a small fenced area containing a grove of dwarf fruit trees. He enjoyed his new freedom, and the succulent browse of fruit tree leaves, native grasses and plants.

I arose early Monday morning, his second day, to check on the little buck. The rich formula, which he drank eagerly, slowed the diarrhea and gave him energy.

I tended the squirrels, and cleaned the raccoon cage. I answered the phone reluctantly as I returned to the house. I thought how nice it would be to have the phone silent for just one day. I listend to the assistant director as she said, "Maggie, this is Sally. I stopped by the Humane Society this morning and heard about the fawn that you have."

"Yes, Sally, our first fawn. I called in a report to you myself. Didn't you pick up all those desperate messages I left over the weekend?"

"I haven't had time to check the machine," she replied tersely.

"Well, he's here, and doing great," I said proudly.

"Maggie, you haven't been given permission to keep fawns. You're not supposed to have him," Sally commented bluntly.

"What? I don't understand. I tried to get help," I answered defensively. "I reported to both you and the director. I had no specific instructions to follow regarding deer. I did the best I could. You don't know the extremes I went through to save him. What should I have done, let him die? Where would I have taken him but here?"

"Well, we've not decided what we intend to do about accepting fawns."

"Okay, Sally, maybe I shouldn't expect a 'thank you' or a 'job well done,' so tell me what you want me to do with this fawn. Where shall I take him for care?" The hurt and anger were evident in my voice.

"I don't know. I guess you'll have to keep him until we find a suitable place," she answered.

"You have a suitable place. I'm the only person in the organization who wants this job. I can do it. I don't understand why you're so hesitant to give me the chance to prove it." Then I continued, "Well, let me know what you decide. Until then, he's doing well right here." I broke off the conversation feeling discouraged and worried about the future of my first fawn.

The fawn grew and flourished as the days and weeks flew by. Soon, other fawns arrived to join him in a territory he considered his own. He lost no time with the usual formalities of circling, smelling and touching noses. The little buck I now called Comanche greeted each new fawn as it came through the gate with a hefty clout on its shoulder with his hoof, promptly establishing himself as chief of the herd. He walked aggressively, with his head held high, as the others followed his leadership willingly.

Animals aren't named because they're considered pets or possessions. They're named only for the purpose of identification. Sometimes their names are derived from the location of the rescue, or from a descriptive injury, or, as in this case, a behavioral characteristic. Comanche's group consisted of Comanche, one other buck, and three does, all of the same age. When released, these fawns raised together will stay together. It's the only family they know.

On the morning of Comanche's release, three volunteers and I closed the anxious fawns into the Fawnmobile for the long ride to their destination. Weeks ago the property owner had given his permission to use his land as a release site. Now I notified him of the time of our arrival. He met us at the entrance to his ranch at the base of the St. Helena mountains. We followed his jeep along a creek and over several miles of bumpy, rocky roads. During most of the trip the fawns lay quietly on the carpeted floor of the truck. However, as we drove into the heart of the mountain, jolting across ruts and rocks, they came to their feet to peer wide-eyed out the windows with their noses held high to catch the scent of fresh mountain air.

We backed the truck up to the water and quietly opened the tailgate. I stepped out of sight so they wouldn't associate the presence of humans with their new wild home. We stood silently, without moving, as our charges impatiently bounded out to freedom. Comanche, the first to leap, led the way down a steep, rocky embankment to the creek. The four other juveniles followed eagerly. They splashed and cavorted in the tumbling water. They drank, then grabbed greedily at the thick, moist blackberry leaves growing profusely along the water's edge.

Climbing into our vehicles, we drove slowly in a broad circle for one quick look of farewell. Beginning their lives of freedom as nature intended, never lifting their eyes to glance in our direction, the five young deer were unmindful of our departure.

Seven fawns lived in the fruit tree enclosure during my first year of involvement with these gentle creatures. Because it became impossible to care for a large variety of animals and find the time, energy and skills it required to do the job well, I discontinued my work with other mammals to learn all I could about the species I had chosen. However, no word came to me from the wildlife director as to whether or not this would be my permanent assignment.

One winter day, feeling insecure in my present situation and needing the assurance that I could continue my work with fawns, I successfully applied for a wildlife permit from the State of California Department of Fish and Game. Fawn Rescue became an official wildlife center. My rehabilitation permit covers all wild mammals. But because of the experience I had accumulated, the pleasure I derived, and the ever increasing demand, Black-tailed fawns and Western Gray squirrels became my specialties. Now all Sonoma County fawns come to this facility. Two large woodland enclosures provide a safe haven for the hundreds of fragile, elegant creatures that Fawn Rescue cares for, and releases year after year.

Comanche, my first fawn, led the way.

2

Fawns and Firemen

Late one summer night I stepped from my bath as the phone rang. Dripping wet, I listened as the County Sheriff's dispatcher relayed the emergency call. A young man, following the sound of incessant cries, had located two fawns trapped in a drainage ditch high on a grassy hillside above the Sonoma trailer park where he lived.

The directions were vague. "A drainage ditch?" I asked. "Is it under the road? Does it have water in it? How am I to find this hole on a hillside in the dark and all alone? Isn't there someone in charge of drainage ditches?"

"I don't know," responded the dispatch operator. "We have your number on file to call for fawn emergencies. Sounds like this might be one."

"I'm not well equipped for this type of rescue. Did you try the Department of Fish and Game?" I began hopefully. "How about the fire department? I've read of times when they've rescued cats from trees."

"This is a weekend night. They're all closed. Besides, the fire department isn't responsible for wildlife," she said wearily. "Our files says this is what you do. You rescue fawns. However, if you can't help..."

"No, wait. I'll see what I can do. Go over the directions once more."

I located a small winding street on my county map and headed south toward Sonoma. I imagined myself climbing the hill with my small flashlight, then dealing with not just one frightened and possibly injured fawn, but two. Two? I thought. How could they both have become trapped? Nevertheless, I knew there was no one else to respond to this call. This late in the season all calls to me were for fawns in trouble. These juveniles were old enough to be out getting hit by cars, caught by dogs, ensnared in fences, and, yes, even trapped in drainage ditches.

As I drove up the hill my headlights flashed on a doe that ran frantically across the road in front of my car. That must be the mother, I thought. The fawns can't be too far from here. I began to drive more slowly, searching for a culvert type drain. I remembered pulling an injured fawn out of one not too long ago. It had been hit by a car and had somehow managed to back into this small drain pipe. I crept through waist-high weeds, approaching out of sight and upwind. Lying on top of the pipe, I reached down over the fawn to make a quick grab for its head before it could back in any farther. It worked that time and perhaps I could use the same method again. Except that this time it was dark and there were two fawns. As I peered into the surrounding darkness I realized how slim my chances were to find these fawns.

Single dwellings in a senior housing complex lined both sides of the narrow street. I stopped to knock on the door of the manager's office thinking he might know of a drainage ditch nearby. I presented my brochure to the man who answered my knock. As I explained my quest, he stared at me oddly. I imagined his thoughts, "What's this little old white-haired lady doing out at this time of night asking about a drainage ditch?" He said he didn't know of one off hand, but he pointed in the direction of a narrow dark driveway leading to a trailer park. "There's a creek down behind the trailers. Could be a drainage ditch there somewhere," the manager suggested. I thanked him for the information. He shook his head in disbelief and closed the door.

As I maneuvered the truck into the small drive, my lights picked up a man leaning against a car in the total darkness. "Well, all I can do is ask," I murmured." I pulled alongside the car, rolled down my window a notch, and asked hopefully. "Hi. Did you call the Sheriff's Department about some fawns?"

A big smile broke over the young man's face. "I sure did. I'm Dan Shelley. I've been waiting for what seems like hours, hoping someone would come. I didn't know what else to do." Dan guided me up a grassy, slippery hill barely visible in front of us. The fawns had ceased crying long before we began our climb.

"I would never have found this place without your help," I said.

"I know, that's why I waited for so long." We stopped suddenly and Dan pointed to the ground in front of us. "They're right here."

I flashed my light down into a deep narrow ten-foot shaft. The four soft brown eyes never blinked as they gazed up into the blinding light. The fawns hung precariously over the covering grill that had been thrown into the shaft along with a number of large rocks. Another two feet of space showed below where the grate was caught. One fawn was wedged on top of the other. They were unable to move.

"This is a drainage ditch? I wasn't looking for a deep shaft."

"They're called drainage ditches," Dan replied. "They're preparing this field for a housing development and this is part of the sewer system."

"I would think the liability would be tremendous if someone was injured because of this open hole," I said. "Luckily, for the property owners, wildlife can't sue for damages." I soon realized that I couldn't provide the help and professional equipment that were obviously needed. "Stay right here, Dan. I'll go for help. It may take a while, but I'll be back with whatever we need to get these fawns out."

I drove about a mile down the highway to the Valley of the Moon Fire Department. Doors were locked; the place was dark. I circled the building and found a light shining through a back window. I rapped with my keys and a startled fireman poked his head out a side door I hadn't noticed. Once inside, I handed him my brochure and explained my problem. "We need to call The Department of Fish and Game for wildlife emergencies," he said as he dialed their dispatch then handed the phone to me.

After listening to my story, the dispatcher said, "Maggie, I know you need help, but every warden in the county is down at the beach. Abalone poachers are keeping us all working overtime. It will be hours before a warden can get up there." Disappointed, I told her I would manage another way.

"Can you just lend me a ladder?" I asked the concerned fireman as I walked back into the room where he waited.

He smiled broadly and replied, "We'll do better than that. I just phoned our battalion chief. He's already on his way to the site. He said he'll meet you there."

As I pulled in below the hillside for the second time that night, two enormous fire trucks roared up to park alongside the Fawnmobile. Nine enthusiastic firemen poured out. "Where are those fawns, Maggie?" asked Chief Markham. Dan once more led the way up the steep incline. Chief Markham focused his powerful beam into the shaft while the firemen peered down at the fawns. "Look at them! They would have died down there, and no one would ever have known," commented one of the men.

"It's okay, little fellows," promised the chief in a soft gentle voice. "We'll have you out of there in no time."

His gentleness brought to mind the time the Eldridge Fire Department called me to pick up a fawn that had been stunned by a car. Several firemen were gathered around the truck. They parted to allow me through. A small fawn lay stretched out in the back breathing deeply through an oxygen mask. The fireman who was monitoring the oxygen grinned up at me and said, "He loves it." I laughed and mentally chided myself for not having my camera. What a classic photo that would have made.

There was a valid reason for this fire department's quick response beyond their compassion for two small fawns. This open shaft was a death trap, and a child could as easily have been the victim.

The firemen moved quickly and efficiently to prepare for the rescue. Within minutes brilliant floodlights transformed the dark hillside into day. Several men concentrated on setting up ladders and pulleys, while others helped carry stretchers and blankets from my truck. The fawns continued to lie quietly in the darkness of the deep shaft.

Hoping to locate tranquilizers, Chief Markham put in a call to Animal Control. Since they had none available, he then phoned Dr. Horton, a local large-animal vet. In spite of the lateness of the hour, both the

Animal Control officer and Dr. Horton hurried to the scene. Dr. Horton came well equipped with tranquilizers and medication. The Animal Control officer pointed toward the hill and said, "I just saw the doe hovering at the edge of those trees as I drove up. I'm surprised she hasn't fled with all this activity going on."

"I saw her there earlier, too, pacing anxiously in and out," replied one of the firemen.

"She's been here all along," I told them. "Spotting her was the one reason I knew the fawns had to be near. It must be hours since they fell, and she's still here." As we prepared for the rescue, I went on, "I've had does come very close and circle me as I picked up their injured fawns. It's pretty awful to have them watch helplessly as you drive off with their young ones. One anxious mother even followed my truck down the road for quite a distance. Luckily, that fawn recovered, and I returned him to his family."

By this time the ladder had been lowered, carefully settled and secured below the grate on the bottom of the shaft. The entrance would be tight for the fireman who readied himself with straps and pulleys. We all gathered in closer. Nine firemen, one vet, one officer, and me, I counted. A dozen concerned people to rescue two little wild creatures. Dr. Horton stepped closer to the hole and said, "I'd better go down first with these tranquilizers. I'll only use enough to make them manageable. I don't want to put them out. It will take effect quickly." He filled the syringes and entered the shaft. As the action focused on the fawns, they gave out piercing screams of terror.

Fully expecting serious abrasions and possible broken bones, we lined up the stretchers near the shaft. We prepared to restrain the two terrified animals to prevent further injury or escape. The fireman, equipped to enter the narrow shaft, stood close awaiting his turn. A few tense seconds later we heard Dr. Horton call out from midway down the hole, "I may as well get them out of here now while I'm wedged in." Balancing precariously on the ladder, he reached around to grab the top fawn. "Here comes number one..." he shouted.

"We've got 'em. We've got 'em," laughed the struggling firemen. The fawns kicked, screamed, and fought frantically as each one, in turn, was hoisted high into the reaching arms of several firemen. We strapped them to the waiting stretchers and examined them thoroughly. Dr. Horton exited from the drainage ditch and pulled medications from his kit. He gave each fawn an injection of antibiotics, then applied ointments to the many cuts and abrasions found on their legs and abdomens.

"Surprisingly, there's no real damage," the vet observed. "No broken bones and the cuts will heal well. There's no reason for them to be taken to Fawn Rescue for care." The mood lightened at once.

"Great news," I said. "Now the trick will be to carry these struggling little guys up the hill where the doe is still waiting." In answer to the crew's incredulous looks, I assured them this final step was necessary. "I want to be sure they're released where they can see the doe and run toward her. Otherwise, they might run out onto the highway. Also, they must be released simultaneously so they'll stay together and not each go in a different direction." The doe had never left in spite of all the noise and human activity—further proof, I observed, that wild mothers do not abandon their young in time of danger.

The firemen laughed as they struggled up the hillside carrying the protesting, alert fawns. We placed them together, side by side, facing in the direction of the anxious mother. Unstrapping one and holding it tightly, we readied the second for freedom. "Ready?" I asked. "Go!" The fawns tore free from our grasp and dashed madly into the trees to join the doe. Within seconds she led them from sight.

We all settled triumphantly on the ground. "I never dreamed a small injured fawn could be so strong," remarked one fireman.

"They will instinctively fight with their last breath," I answered. "Sick ones that can barely move will somehow find strength to get to their feet and run fast enough to make them difficult to catch. Their fear gives them the power to fight to escape."

"Well, I've learned some interesting things about deer tonight. We seldom deal with wildlife," another said. "A call to rescue a cat is usually the extent of our animal calls."

"You've learned something about the spirit of wildlife, and I've learned about the kindness of people," I said.

Before packing up their equipment for departure, one of the fire department crew entered the shaft and attached a pulley to the heavy drainage ditch grill. After some struggle they managed to free the tightly wedged cover and hoist it out of the shaft. Finally, they secured the drainage ditch against further accidents.

The next morning I stopped by the trailer park where Dan Shelley lived to thank him for his role in the rescue. I hadn't seen him leave the night before. The park manager came out to say the trio of deer had been spotted foraging on the hillside. One fawn limped slightly, she said.

Because Dan cared enough to follow the desperate cries of the fawns, the story ended happily. Our valley is abundant with people who care.

3
The Stray

A few years ago Mr. and Mrs. Hal Fisher purchased ten acres of wilderness for the sole purpose of enjoying quiet weekends far from San Francisco and the hectic pace of their workday world. Never tiring of the routine, each Friday they changed into casual camp clothes and headed for two days of rest in their secluded sanctuary. Relieved of all the demands of business, their days were filled with reading, fishing and relaxing. No jarring ring of phones reached into their haven. No clamor of traffic disturbed the tranquility of the campsite. Dense underbrush surrounded the small clearing where they parked the compact trailer and set up camp. Their limited view looked into a tight grove of oak, madrone, bay and fir.

As the sun burned through the early morning mist the two campers awakened from a refreshing sleep in the bracing country air. They were hungry and looked forward to their usual leisurely breakfast by the campfire. The aroma of fried potatoes, scrambled eggs, sausage and toast drifted into the trees surrounding their campsite. The last drop of coffee had been poured and enjoyed, and after the clean-up they tossed all remnants of the meal into the cooling campfire.

Fisher sat on the leaf-strewn ground checking his gear, preparing for an hour or two of fishing at the river, while his wife anticipated a morning of lying alone under the cool canopy of trees to read a newly purchased mystery. The incessant chatter of a squirrel and the warning tap of his foot on a limb high overhead alerted the couple to a sudden slight rustle in the brush. As they glanced curiously in that direction, a thin, scruffy fawn darted past them directly toward the now cold campfire, pushed its nose into the ashes and devoured the discarded remains of breakfast. None of the scraps went untouched—cold potatoes, pieces of dried toast, even bits of egg that were covered with coffee grounds. The couple stared in amazement as the fawn searched desperately for more food. "What in the world...?" remarked Fisher softly, afraid of frightening the hungry young deer.

Mrs. Fisher reached over to lift an apple from a basket sitting beside her chair. She gently rolled it in the direction of the fawn. Showing no fear of the sudden movement, the small creature ran quickly toward the apple and began to consume it ravenously. "It seems starved," she whispered to her husband. "I wonder why, with all these green things growing all over the place? I thought that's what deer eat."

"It acts tame, don't you think? It shows no sign of fear."

"I wonder if it's someone's pet that wandered off?" Mrs. Fisher asked.

"Out here? Where would it have wandered from? There isn't a house within miles," Fisher reasoned.

"Yes, that's true," his wife responded as she stood up slowly then moved cautiously toward the trailer. "I'm going to see what I can find to feed it besides garbage. Can you imagine how starved it must be to eat that awful mess?" The fawn glanced in her direction as she walked away but continued to munch the apple with vigor. Mrs. Fisher emerged again, almost immediately, with two slices of wheat bread and a ripe Bartlett pear. "This should be good for it," she said as she took a hesitant step in the fawn's direction. The hungry animal unhesitatingly took the bread from her hand and finished it along with the fruit. Its appetite appeased, it curled up beside Mrs. Fisher's chair and fell into a deep satisfied sleep.

"Whatever is going on?" she asked in wonder. "You must be right. It does act tame. Do you suppose someone raised it, then dropped it off out here thinking it could survive on its own?"

"That's my guess," her husband answered. "But now what do we do with our little stray? It appears to have adopted us. You know how that works, once you feed it, it's yours." He laughed as he collected his gear and moved toward the car.

"I remember seeing something on TV about a place around here that takes care of fawns. When we get home tomorrow night I'll see if I can locate it and give them a ring," she called after him.

"The fawn may just decide to wander off before then," he answered as he closed the car door and backed around the trailer to head for his favorite spot along the river.

Mrs. Fisher tried to concentrate on the novel, but her attention kept returning to the wonder of the young wild creature that had taken up residence in their campsite. "If it's still here when we're ready to leave, I'll put out the food we have left to hold it over until we return next weekend. I'll call the fawn center Monday and see what they make of this strange situation," she murmured.

When the fawn awoke Mrs. Fisher offered it fruit and cereal. It showed no inclination to return to the wild and seemed content with its new life as a camper.

Sunday afternoon the two weekend visitors reluctantly packed up for the long three-hour drive back to the city. They placed food for the stray beside the trailer. The fawn followed the car part way down the long dirt road, then turned back toward the security of the camp as the couple disappeared out of sight.

Early Monday morning Mrs. Fisher called the local Humane Society hoping to find a phone number for the fawn facility.

Pleased with her success, she immediately put through her important call. She explained their incredible weekend experience to me as I listened intently to every detail. "Surely this isn't normal behavior. Something has to be very wrong with the situation this fawn has found itself in, don't you agree?" she asked.

"You bet," I answered. "This is a classic case of why the general public shouldn't attempt to raise wildlife," I told her. I went on to explain that people without wildlife training don't know at what age an animal may be released safely, or what skills it needs to cope alone in the wilderness. They don't realize that a young one must be taught to recognize the food it will find and to be aware of predators. These people tire of the responsibility of raising the animal, or it begins to show aggression as it matures, so it's simply put out in some wild area to fend as best it can. "This fawn is one of the few lucky enough to find help," I said. "The others die alone and unaided."

Mrs. Fisher continued, "We hope it won't wander away, thinking it has been deserted again, before we get back next weekend. We left a lot of food for it, which is all we could think to do. If it's still there when we return next weekend, I'll contact you."

"I wish you had called me when it first came into your camp, and it would already be in my care. But now, to drive a hundred miles to try to locate your camp, then find the fawn gone would help no one," I said, filled with concern.

"Yes, I had no idea it would stay so long or I would have tried to locate you at once," Mrs. Fisher said.

During the next few busy days, my thoughts continued to dwell on the small creature that, I hoped, still waited for help in the deep woods.

Saturday morning I was on my way to the fawn pen where my charges waited for their 7:30 a.m. feeding when the phone rang. Twelve hungry fawns looked toward me expectantly as I set down the heavy tray filled with bottles of formula. I retraced my steps to answer the call. "Fawn Rescue. This is Maggie," I began.

"Oh, Maggie, I'm glad you're there. I had to drive over ten miles to find a public phone. This is Mrs. Fisher. The fawn greeted us like old friends last night. She didn't seem stressed, just hungry. Now what do we do?"

"Give me directions and I'll leave as soon as the fawns are fed. I'm amazed she's still there. Keep a close watch on her. We can't risk losing her now," I cautioned.

"Slight danger of that. We couldn't run her off. She thinks this is her home," she laughed.

Picking up the tray of bottles once again, I ran down the steps to feed the waiting line of eager fawns. I pushed the bottles into the racks and within seconds every drop of formula had disappeared. Soon the bottles were rinsed and stacked in the dishwasher. I'd have to leave at once and travel fast to be back from Mendocino County in time for the next feeding.

Cutting through the back hills to avoid traffic, I sped north on Highway 101. A few miles beyond Ukiah the exit sign indicated my westward turnoff. The tight winding climb along the river, in unfamiliar territory, seemed much longer than I had anticipated. Could I have passed my landmark? I wondered. This isolated canyon is no place to be lost. The Fishers have no phone. I remembered how far Mrs. Fisher drove to call me. I pulled to a stop at a small turnout on the road to check my scribbled directions that lay on the seat beside me. Well, I can't be lost, I assured myself. There's no place else to go. I slowed at each cutoff road to peer into the deepening woods. Finally the description Mrs. Fisher had given me matched my surroundings. Yes, a small creek to the left, a sharp turn to the right, then straight down a steep dirt road, winding through trees and boulders. The Fawnmobile bumped and jolted over ruts and rocks. The only road ended at the Fishers' campsite. I made the sharp turn to park beside their trailer and climb out of the truck to stretch after the hot two-hour drive, enjoying the feel of the fresh cool breeze.

The middle-aged couple smiled a warm greeting as they rose from their chairs. Behind them bounced a small spotted animal. Before any words of introduction were exchanged, I swooped up the scrawny, undernourished fawn crawling with parasites, and placed her in the back of the truck. No chance for her to bolt, I explained. She calmly gazed at us through the camper window. After our introductions, I accepted a cola and sat down to listen once again as the relieved couple reviewed the entire story of their experience with the charming visitor that had appeared out of the forest seeking help.

How a tame spotted fawn, not yet of weaning age, came to be found so far from civilization remained a total mystery. How unthinkable, we agreed, that anyone could have driven it to this remote area, put it out and expected one this young to cope alone. It would have died soon of stress and starvation. “Perhaps a little woodland god led it to your camp,” I said to the Fishers with a smile.

After earnestly thanking the couple for their concern, I began my long journey south to Fawn Rescue. Although anxious to bring the young doe back to health by introducing her to a natural and nourishing diet, I knew removing the parasites would be the first important step. Combing fleas, ticks and lice from her thin body, then dusting it with a repellent would be necessary before she could enter the pen.

That night Nutmeg settled down in an isolated section of the enclosure. She refused the bottle offered her, but drank warm formula from a bowl with enthusiasm. Within two days she joined a group of four fawns of the same age. At each feeding she stood silently in the background intently studying her hungry companions as they ran to the feeder to grab a nipple and suck fervently. Nutmeg licked her lips as she watched longingly. I lifted her face to the nipple that protruded from the feeder, but she seemed not to understand the concept. I tried holding a bottle in my hand and placing the nipple directly into her mouth. She made an attempt to suck, she seemed to need the sucking, nurturing experience. But each time she had difficulty trying to nurse. She pulled away in frustration to return to drinking from the bowl as she had no doubt been taught.

One day, as I sat motionless, watching from outside the pen, she suddenly ran toward the feeders in desperation, and as the other fawns grabbed for a space to eat, she grabbed, too. She leaned forward into the nipple and closed her eyes as she sucked. Her enraptured expression left no doubt that this action fulfilled a natural longing. Thereafter, each time Nutmeg nursed from the bottle, she closed her eyes in pure enjoyment. The bowl became a thing of the past, and she continued to nurse until weaned.

By mid-August a mature, well adjusted, healthy young doe and her four companions had no further need for the security provided by Fawn Rescue. They were released as a family on private, protected land. One by one they leaped impatiently out of the back of the camper. At home in the wilderness, they bounded joyfully across an open field to freedom with never a backward glance.

4
Baby Doll

I returned home at 3:15 a.m. after driving ninety-five miles into the remote wilderness of the Cazadero hills to pick up an ill fawn. I lay in bed mentally reviewing the trip that began with a midnight phone call. The man who called explained that he had just investigated a loud thump which reverberated against the back of his hillside cabin. The beam from his flashlight shone on a very young fawn sprawled against the house. It didn't move, he said, and it appeared to be in shock. So he left it lying there and rushed inside to call Fawn Rescue.

"Finding the house will be difficult," Jake Duncan explained. "We sit back off the main road. Just park in front of the village market and honk your horn. I'll watch for you and come down the hill to meet you. How long will it take to get here?"

I estimated I could be there in an hour and a half. "Are you sure about honking the horn at this hour?" I asked.

"It'll be fine," he laughed.

Ten minutes later I was on my way. Even though I had traveled these same roads often during the daylight hours, the drive west toward the beach looked unfamiliar after dark. I eventually swung north onto remote Austin Creek Road. I could see nothing along the twisting road but the dark silhouettes of towering redwoods bordering the creek. The town seemed farther back in the hills than I remembered. After rounding a long, smooth curve in the road, I entered the tiny town of Cazadero. It was all dark. I parked by the darkened grocery store and gingerly beeped my horn. Beep. Beep...beep. No answer. Not a sound broke the stillness, not even a barking dog. I sat for a few minutes wondering uneasily if I had the right place, then cruised slowly through the small town once more and circled back. Yes, I decided, this is the only market. I parked in front again, and this time pushed harder and longer on the horn. I wondered how many homes there might be nearby in the darkness and how many neighbors I was disturbing. My thoughts were interrupted by a shout, and I saw a flashlight swinging in an arc from the top of the steep hill.

"Okay, I'll be right down," a deep male voice called.

I stepped from the truck to look high up into the blackness. My eyes followed the tiny flicker of light as it moved unsteadily along a winding path, then down a series of turning, twisting steps.

"Hi, I'm Jake Duncan," a voice said from behind a flashlight's beam. "You made good time. The fawn is still against the house where I found her. We were afraid to move her." We climbed steadily as he talked. One final step led us into the open door of the small hillside home. "Come on in. Can't get to the back without going clear through the house. The hill gets in the way," he explained.

As we wandered through the house, several adults stood nodding their greetings in silence. Jake led the way from the service porch into a tight passage along the back of the house. He flashed his light on the spot where a tiny fawn lay in shock. "Here she is. Slid clear down that steep hill and hit the house — hard," he said.

Bending to pick up the small, still creature, I wrapped her in a blanket. "Here, let me carry her down those long steps," Jake offered. He turned to re-enter his home with the small bundle cradled in his arms. A slim woman stepped forward to hand me a ten dollar bill.

"For gas," she said with a gentle smile.

"You don't need to pay me. I don't charge for my service," I said. This family looked as though money was not easy to come by.

"It's not pay. It took a lot of gas to drive all this way. It's all we can do to help," another member of the group offered. I took the money and thanked them for caring.

It began to rain as Jake and I wound our way back down the stairs in the dark with one flashlight between us. No lights came on in the nearby homes in spite of our voices and the flickering light. No dogs barked. I placed the fawn gently on a bed of blankets. She shivered as I covered her.

The Animal Emergency Center, half way across the county, would be the only help available at this late hour. The vet on duty had helped me many nights in the past with many such emergencies. This time she supplied me with antibiotics to combat an advanced case of pneumonia, but offered little hope for this fawn's recovery.

Back at home, satisfied the fawn had been settled indoors for her long period of convalescence, I undressed for bed at 3:15 a.m. I slid gratefully under the covers and fell into a deep sleep. I thought it must be morning when the shrill ring of the phone awoke me for the second time that night. I glanced at the clock. It read 5 a.m. I picked up the receiver with reluctance, feeling certain this call meant another trip out into the rain. A frantic but determined woman explained that while driving along the edge of a small state park near Calistoga, a doe leaped from behind a bush and ran directly into the path of her car. She stopped to find the doe unconscious, but alive. The woman and her companion wrapped the doe in her car blanket and managed to lift it into the back seat of the vehicle. Now she wanted to transfer the animal to me before it regained consciousness. To save time we agreed to meet at a half-way point in front of Safeway in half an hour. My second grocery store rendezvous tonight, I thought.

As I rounded the corner to enter the Safeway parking lot, I spotted the woman pacing in the distance. When I pulled to a stop beside her, she said, "The doe's eyes are beginning to twitch, and she's moving her head a little. Does that mean she'll be okay?"

"I'll let you know," I answered with a worried glance at the injured deer. We managed, with difficulty, to slide and lift her out of the small vehicle and into my camper where she could rest comfortably. I wrote down the woman's name, address and phone number, and the exact location where the doe had been picked up. I promised to keep her informed. "Next time, please pull the animal off to the side of the road, then call for help," I said as I closed the tailgate. "You put yourself and your passenger at great risk, Miss Keller, when you put this adult deer in your car. But thanks for stopping. So many drivers continue on, leaving the injured animal along the road to die. This one should live because of your concern."

At Fawn Rescue I examined the still unconscious doe. She didn't look badly injured. No broken bones, no blood. I administered medication for head trauma and propped her up on her sternum so she could breath comfortably. I wedged blankets tightly on either side, covered her, then left her in the carpeted truck for the night. I crawled into bed at dawn exhausted.

Two hours later I forced myself to get to my feet, dress, feed fifteen fawns, then check my two latest charges. The small ill fawn lay dead under her blanket. Pneumonia, the slide against the house, and the trauma were more than her young body could overcome.

Outside, I peeked quietly around the corner of the open garage door. The doe stood strong and alert inside the camper. She sensed my presence at once and raised her head to look in my direction. Her stance clearly said, "Let me out of here...now."

"You bet, old girl," I assured her under my breath. "We'll have you back in the park within the hour." The phone rang as I closed the door to leave. "No, not now. Not another emergency," I begged wearily. I went back into the house to the phone.

"Is this the lady that takes fawns?" a man asked in a strained, tense voice.

"Yes, what's wrong?" I asked him, wide awake, alert and sensing trouble.

"I live in a condo. I've had this baby deer here for a while. My little girl just loves to play with it. It's her baby doll while my wife's at work."

"You're raising a fawn in your condo?" I asked incredulously. "Where did you get it? How long have you had it? What are you feeding it?"

"Well, we found it. We haven't had it for long," he answered evasively. "We're mixing some kind of formula for it. Probably the same thing the baby gets. But, listen, I've got a real problem, and I want out of this mess right away."

"Give me your name, address, and phone number, then tell me about it," I insisted, afraid of losing him.

"I'm Jim Kormer. A neighbor reported me to the Department of Fish and Game. There's been a warden prowling around here for a couple of days. I don't answer the door, but now I can't even go out of the house. I'm tired of playing games. The neighbor told me there's a thousand dollar fine if I'm caught with this fawn. Is that true?" he asked.

"I can guarantee you there will be a good sized fine. Especially since the warden has had to spend so much time trying to get that fawn from you," I answered with satisfaction, making sure he would relinquish the fawn.

"Well, if you get down here before that warden does, will I still be fined?"

"I'll come as quickly as I can to pick up the fawn, Mr. Kormer, but I can't speak for the Department. They'll handle the citation in their own way. If they get there before I do, tell them I'm on my way so they'll wait for me," I told the nervous man. Then I remembered my truck was occupied by an anxious doe waiting to be free. "Oh, wait, Mr. Kormer. I have to make a quick run to release a doe. Then I'll head directly down to Rohnert Park. It will take me a little over an hour," I calculated.

"No," Kormer said emphatically, his voice rising in anger. "I'll take this fawn and dump it somewhere. It isn't worth having to pay a fine over. You come now, or it won't be here when you do get here. I'll not risk being fined for an animal."

"After making a pet of it and telling me how much you all love it, surely you aren't serious, Mr. Kormer? You couldn't do that, could you?" I confronted him angrily.

"Don't try me," he said.

"All right, I'll leave this instant. Give me a half hour." I slammed down the phone without waiting for his answer.

I sped through the pass, over the hill, and down the busy freeway. The doe lay quietly on the carpeted floor of the truck during the entire trip. I circled the complex looking for the correct condo, parked, then ran up to the door and knocked.

The door opened a crack. "Yea?" a man asked.

I held my brochure in front of his face. "Fawn Rescue," I said.

"Oh, great. You got here first," he smiled, greatly relieved. The door opened wide. I stepped inside as he scooped up the thin, fragile fawn with one hand and shoved her into my arms. I held her from me and stared in amazement. A diaper snugly covered the bottom half of her body, while four pink booties flashed wildly in the air as she kicked. I looked at her aghast, then said, "I can understand the diaper, but why the booties?"

"Well, I didn't want Baby Doll tearing up the carpet with those hoofs. Pretty neat, huh? I made them myself," he answered proudly.

I couldn't make it out the door fast enough with the diapered fawn tucked securely in my arms. Surprisingly, even though I had stopped, the doe continued to lie in the truck, apparently at ease. I placed the tiny fawn in an airline carrier beside me on the seat. Kormer suddenly emerged from the condo carrying a small sack. "Oh, wait," he said. "I have its food. I sure don't want it around here."

"No thanks, Mr. Kormer, that's not what she'll be eating from now on." I waved goodby, then paused a few blocks down the street to check the doe, concerned that she hadn't moved for so long. I peeked through the side window. She began to rise aggressively. "We're going, we're going," I said. I followed the highway north once more, then turned east over the mountain to Calistoga. The diapered fawn slept soundly on the front seat while the doe lay patiently in the back.

In less than an hour I pulled up to the state park entrance gate to explain my mission to the rangers. They stared at my cargo in wonder and motioned me on, pointing to a nearby field where the doe could be returned to familiar territory once more. I circled the field to find a spot to park near the woods. Reaching behind the seat for my camera, I congratulated myself on having the rare opportunity to get some good release photos of an adult deer. I opened the hatch, and before the tailgate was completely down, the determined doe leaped past me through the opening. She made one short bound onto a well-known path and vanished into the trees. No photos.

"Come on, Baby Doll," I said. "Let's go home to Fawn Rescue where you'll be hanging out for a few months. Just wait until you see the other fawns. You've never seen one of your own species, have you? You don't even know you're a fawn, but you will." On down the road I continued my one sided conversation. "We'll report to the Department of Fish and Game that you're safe, then you'll have real fawn food for lunch. And just think, you'll be using dirt now instead of a disposable diaper." Sleeping soundly, Baby Doll never heard a word.

A message on my answering machine asked me to get in touch with the Department. Our warden wanted to set up a time for me to go with him to pick up a fawn in Rohnert Park. "I think I already have that fawn, Jeannie," I assured the dispatch operator. We compared names and addresses and agreed the fawn was Baby Doll.

A few minutes later the phone rang. "Maggie, this is Paul. How did you ever get that fawn? I've been after it for days," the warden laughed.

"I can take no credit," I answered. "The man actually shoved her into my arms. He couldn't wait to be rid of her. You had him terrified of the citation, Paul. So no doubt he's learned a good lesson."

"I still intend to pay him a visit to reinforce the lesson. Glad the fawn's safe," the warden replied.

"You should have seen her when she saw her first fawn, Paul. Total amazement and disbelief. Don't tell me animals can't show expression. When she finally found the courage to touch noses with one, she was sure. She's sticking close to the group now that she knows she's a real deer."

5
Rat-tail Combs

During the beginning years of my work with wildlife, raccoons were one of my first assignments. I enjoyed caring for these delightful, intelligent babies. However, I soon learned they are born wild, and mature raccoons are dangerous when they become old enough to demand their freedom. In our outreach programs we continually warn the public that wild animals do not make good pets.

As I directed my limited time and energy toward my chosen specialty of raising injured and orphaned fawns, I discontinued working with other species of wildlife. But a neighbor who also cared for wildlife called to ask for my help in dealing with a situation involving raccoons. Norma told me she had received an odd call that needed investigating, but she didn't want to handle it alone.

A friend of hers, she said, heard an advertisement on a small local radio station announcing the sale of Rat-Tail Combs, for twenty dollars each. Norma's friend called the listed number out of curiosity. The man who answered her call explained that he sells raccoons. He said the coded message informs hunters, who use these helpless creatures to train their hunting dogs, that he has a new supply of raccoons for sale. The distraught woman immediately called Norma, who assured her that selling wildlife is illegal, and promised to investigate. Norma and I agreed that the seller must know the law, why else would he need to advertise in code? We were amazed that anyone would be careless enough to advertise the sale of wildlife on the radio, even in code.

We decided to investigate at once, before the raccoons were sold. After setting a cage in the back of the pickup, I drove the two miles to Norma's house. She stood waiting beside the road, jumped into the truck, and we headed toward the southeast corner of the county. Few buildings dotted this open territory. Miles of vineyards, laden with grapes ready for harvesting, covered the land. During the drive, we discussed ways to convince the raccoon owner to let us see the animals without revealing our real mission. We decided to pose as buyers who wanted a pet. We would then have tangible evidence for the Department of Fish and Game.

The ill-kept house, located on a small back road, was surrounded with weeds. A hard-featured, middle-aged man walked across the field to greet us. His manner was abrupt. "Yea?", he said.

"I've been told you have raccoons for sale. Do you think one would make a good pet?" I asked him.

The surly man brightened at once. "Oh, sure," he responded enthusiastically. "Come on back and I'll show them to you. I only have a few for sale right now. All the rest sold in a hurry. I'll have more soon, though." I asked his name. "I'm Vince Scutter," he answered.

"How is it that you have these raccoons for sale?" I questioned. "Did you find a family of them on your property?"

"Oh, no. I've been doing this for sixteen years. I always keep one female to breed. Have to get rid of them as they wear out," he laughed. "I sell all the young ones to hunters. They buy them up as fast as I can raise them. Use them to teach their dogs to follow a scent, you know."

I cringed at the mental picture his words conjured. He led us into a section of bare field devoid of trees, brush, or shade. There, five large raccoons crowded into a small three-by-four foot cage perched on wooden legs. Three sides were built of filth-encrusted wood. The front was wire, matted with fetid balls of hair. A smaller identical cage housed an ill-looking pregnant female.

"There's no shade, Mr. Scutter. They must suffer from the heat," I said, attempting to keep my voice calm and free of the revulsion I felt.

"Oh, they're used to it. They have water."

"Where? The bowls are all empty," I countered.

"Well, I turn the hose on them once in a while. Kind of cleans out the cages and fills the bowls at the same time. They keep dumping everything over. Not too smart. Food doesn't last long either, the way they fight over it." Not wanting to argue with a potential customer, and hoping to get on with business, Scutter shrugged and walked closer to the cages. Stench rose from the feces-covered ground beneath the cages. As he approached, the stressed raccoons growled in fear and cowered to the back of the small cage.

"Are you sure they'll make good pets?" I persisted. "They look dangerous to me."

Suddenly Scutter's temper flared. "There's nothing dangerous about them. You want one, or not? They're twenty dollars each."

"Twenty dollars? Is that a good price? I've never bought a raccoon before."

"Twenty dollars is what I always get. Take it or leave it. I won't have any problem selling these," he answered impatiently.

Needing all the information I could get, I asked, "Are they healthy animals? How do I know I'm not giving you twenty dollars for a sick animal?"

"They're as healthy as can be. I guarantee it," he snarled, obviously wanting to be rid of me.

"Would you put that in writing, so I can get my money back if it dies?"

"In writing?" he asked incredulously.

"Sure. I'll buy one right now if you give me a guarantee. I'll even pass the word along about you." I glanced innocently over at Norma.

"Well, I guess I could do that," he said, anticipating other sales.

Norma had been standing in the background listening, but not participating in the conversation. Now she ran to get the cage and the twenty dollars from the truck.

As I held open the door of my carrier, the breeder reached into his cage to roughly grab a raccoon by the tail. The terrified animal screamed and tightened its claws on the wire. Scutter cursed and pulled the raccoon's tail viciously, finally pulling it loose from the cage. He swung it in a circular motion attempting to push it into my cage. The frightened creature spread its legs to grasp the edge of the door. Scutter, still cursing, pulled the animal back and swung it into the air. As it passed his leg, it lunged at the angry man's thigh and took a strong hold with its teeth. Blood gushed through his pant leg. Scutter shouted obscenities, grabbed the head of the raccoon, and squeezed the sides of its mouth, trying to force the terrified creature to let go. Once free of the animal's grip, he flung it savagely into my cage.

"The crazy thing bit me!" he said in fury.

"Yes," I answered, filled with loathing and fury that matched his own. "Perhaps you had better take care of the wound while I write out a receipt for you to sign." I was determined to shut down this man's operation, and I knew we would need a strong case. I had difficulty proceeding. I longed to help the still-captive raccoons, but I realized if I lost control now, the whole rescue would be lost, and none would be saved. We must have the evidence to stop him permanently by law.

Scutter ran into the house while Norma made a second trip back to the truck for a tablet. On it I wrote the date, the time of day, and the phrase, "Sold—one healthy raccoon for twenty dollars."

When the breeder came out of the house, still cursing, I handed him the receipt to sign. He signed without a thought, without even glancing at its content. Only then did Norma hand him the money. I said, in parting, "You'd better have a doctor look at that bite," knowing he wouldn't dare try to explain to a doctor what had happened. He shook his head impatiently and hurried into the house, slamming the door behind him.

I dropped Norma off at her home, then transferred the raccoon to a wildlife refuge where it would be safe and well cared for. Later, after I fed the fawns, I called the Department of Fish and Game to leave a report. Early the following morning a call came from Hilda Sims, the local game warden.

Appalled by the raccoon situation, and provoked that Norma and I had undertaken this project on our own, she explained the procedures. We had overstepped our authority, she said sternly. "This problem should have been reported to the Department before you decided to take charge. The confiscation of wildlife is not within your jurisdiction. We do the investigating, then take the proper steps." She continued, "I can see how you were moved to help, but next time, just report to us, and we'll take care of it. Now, give me the address, Maggie, and I'll get right over to Mr. Scutter's to pick up the rest of those raccoons."

Properly enlightened, I apologized. It had not occurred to either Norma or me that we were out of line. In our eagerness to rescue wildlife, we learned a lesson that served us well in the future.

Shortly, Warden Sims pulled into Scutter's driveway. Scutter, seeing the emblem on the Department's truck, came out to greet her at the gate. She identified herself and stated her mission. The raccoon breeder escorted her back to the cages. He was cooperative, and relinquished the animals without comment. He helped her transfer them to the Department's cages and carry them out to the transport truck. The warden presented him with a citation for illegal possession of wildlife.

Warden Sims drove directly to Animal Control with the confiscated animals and placed them under the care of their veterinarian. Our rescued raccoon from the previous evening bit the vet during its initial examination. The Health Department put it under quarantine immediately. The authorities permitted this raccoon, being held as evidence for the trial, to remain in the wildlife enclosure in the country during its period of confinement.

I wrote a testimonial statement for the court. In my letter I explained the conditions under which these animals were forced to live. I pointed out Scutter's brutality in dealing with the raccoon. I continued: "Mr. Scutter assured me this raccoon would make a wonderful pet, when, in fact, it presented a real danger. A child could lose a hand while attempting to touch one of these mistreated, vicious animals.

"At no time did Mr. Scutter caution me about the danger I might encounter while owning a wild animal. Even after the raccoon bit deeply into Mr. Scutter's leg, he permitted me to purchase it as a pet. He showed no concern for the raccoon, nor for the public to whom he was selling these visibly ill creatures." I finished by urging the court to stop this inhumane and illegal sale of wildlife.

At the trial weeks later, Municipal Judge Anna Carter placed Mr. Vince Scutter under three years probation, fined him one thousand dollars, and ordered that he perform one hundred hours of community service with the Humane Society.

In addition, the court ordered him to make restitution to the veterinarian who took charge of the animals, and give a one-hundred dollar donation to the wildlife organization for whom Norma worked as a volunteer. She could then be reimbursed for the twenty dollars she had paid to Mr. Scutter for the purchase of the raccoon.

All six of the confiscated animals displayed dangerous temperaments and suffered severely from an incurable skin disease. Regrettably, this irreversible diagnosis, and the pain they would have for the remainder of their lives, left no merciful alternative but euthanasia.

6
Reunited

One of the most rewarding experiences in the rescue of wildlife occurs when a newborn, separated from its mother, is successfully reunited with her to live once again under her expert care. The myth still persists that a wild mother will not accept its young once it has been touched by humans. This rumor has been proven many times over to be untrue.

Often, I have returned baby birds to their nests, at times even placing them in a different container if the birth nest is not accessible or has been destroyed. Placing the chirping baby in a shoe box as close as possible to the original nest will attract the parent birds, who resume the feeding of their offspring most willingly.

*

One chilly morning a gray fox, stunned by a blow from a passing car, lay unconscious on the shoulder of the road. Her two kits curled against her seeking comfort. Creeping in from behind, I lowered my long-handled net gently down over the three furry bodies. The mother never stirred. The babies crouched even closer to her in an attempt to hide.

My luck held as I reached under the net with my heavily gloved hand, to retrieve each kit in turn and place them in a small carrier. I then lifted the adult fox, net still over her body, and laid her carefully in a separate carrier for her trip to the vet. Dr. Patton gave her an injection to combat the swelling and shock brought on by her concussion.

During her convalescence, all three foxes lived together in a large outdoor cage in a wooded area of Fawn Rescue. I held and fed the young kits for the first two days of their captivity. The ill mother made no attempt to interfere. But on the third day, she had recovered enough to resume the responsibility of their care and did so as though there had been no interruption. Each day she gained strength and one day began to pace—an indication of a wild animal's need to be free. Early one evening I left the cage door open and sometime after dark, the fully recovered vixen led her young ones out into the hills to freedom.

*

A lactating mother raccoon, unwelcome in a meticulously kept yard where she had ventured to grub for worms, had been trapped and delivered to Fawn Rescue by the wrathful property owner. Angrily, he insisted that she be relocated far away from his home. He vowed to destroy her if she returned. Her two hungry, crying babies remained where she had left them. I confined the mother overnight in hope of capturing the young ones, as well.

The following night both hungry babies willingly entered the live trap in search of food, and I received an urgent call to pick them up. Pleased to have them in my possession so quickly, I hurried back to Fawn Rescue to reunite the family. They scurried into the cage where the eager mother waited. She ran to touch and fondle them, emitting soft greetings of welcome in obvious joy as the squealing babies settled down to nurse without hesitation.

Relocating wildlife is not an ideal solution. Other wildlife soon replace the animal that has been removed. The relocated creature must compete in a territory already claimed by others and must search for its food in an unfamiliar area. However, having no alternative, we immediately settled this contented family in a protected location beside a clear and well stocked stream. We fervently hoped they would adapt to their new home.

*

I recall many unforgettable experiences when I have reunited fawns with their searching and anxious mothers.

A heavy construction crew reported to work in Fountain Grove one morning to find, amid the enormous building and earth-moving equipment, a small fawn standing frozen with fear at the sudden roar of the power tools and engines. One young man quickly scooped up the terrified fawn and called Animal Control from his portable phone. Animal Control transferred his call to Fawn Rescue, and I left for the construction site at once. Upon arrival I found the trembling fawn curled in the seat of a bulldozer parked at the edge of the deafening activity.

In order to make room for this new housing development, an entire wooded area, once home to a number of wild creatures, had been destroyed. However, a short distance away, a small grove of trees still remained. This oak, fir and dense brush provided a slim corridor through which most of the wildlife escaped. These animals, driven from their home, must attempt to adapt to a new life in unfamiliar territory.

As I held the protesting, very vocal fawn tightly against my chest, I glanced into the edge of the trees where the young man indicated the doe had run. I glimpsed her frantically pacing and jumping along the perimeter of the small grove. Her head flipped back in panic each time the fawn bleated. While moving swiftly up over the huge mounds of freshly piled earth and rocks, the loose dirt shifted under my feet. I lost my balance and fell, sliding on my back, down the far side of the hill.

The fawn cried sharply while I clutched him to me more tightly as we slid. Good, I thought. Keep screaming little one so your mom won't run away as we approach. The fawn cooperated in fine style as the doe leaped nervously back and forth through the trees. Finally landing at the bottom of the slope, I struggled to my feet still gripping the protesting fawn firmly. Crossing a narrow, and, as yet, unplowed field, I entered the edge of the woods.

The doe crashed through the brush a short distance in front of me, then circled around behind, always staying near. I set the fawn on its feet in a small clearing, then backed away. The doe came charging into the clearing and touched her nose briefly against her baby. Never slowing her pace, she trotted by me with the fawn leaping behind her, then vanished instantly into the trees.

On another occasion, a fawn became lodged under the deck of a house built on the slope of a steep hillside. The fawn had no turning room in the tightly enclosed spot. Its cries of panic brought the owner of the house out onto the deck to investigate. In answer to his summons, I drove the winding roads up into the sprawling hills above Glen Elen.

While parking, I could clearly hear the bleat of the distressed fawn. The cries ceased as I crawled under the structure and squeezed into the small space where the animal was wedged. It hugged the earth in silence, as fawns do naturally when sensing danger. Scarcely able to touch the frightened animal with my finger tips, I inched forward just enough to secure a firm hold on its tiny hips and maneuver him free. As I grasped him tightly, he kicked and bleated shrilly in protest.

Just then, in answer to his cry, a large doe appeared at the edge of the dense brush at the bottom of the hill. She watched intently as I examined the young deer carefully for abrasions or broken bones. Aware of her fawn's location, she could do nothing to help it out of its predicament, but, nevertheless, maintained her vigil nearby.

The owner of the house watched with interest from his vantage point on the deck. I set the fawn firmly on the ground facing the swiftly advancing doe. Her posture made it clear she would no longer tolerate human interference. Ears back, legs stiff, she walked determinedly in our direction with her head thrust forward. The tiny deer leaped from my hands and headed downhill into the field, but made a sudden turn away from the doe. The harried mother immediately changed course to intercept the wayward fawn and met him in midfield. She nudged him in recognition, then set off at a slow trot, leading him to safety at the opposite end of the woods. The fawn followed closely on her heels, leaping high on his spindly legs over small clumps of grass, across the field, and out of sight.

*

Mrs. Paul Breck, my neighbor, called recently to tell me they often watched a group of deer browsing in the backyard which borders on a creek. A path on the opposite bank of the creek leads up the hill into Annadel State Park. This morning, when the herd moved down into the creek area then vanished into the park, they left behind a small fawn sleeping under a manzanita bush. "It's been here for hours, Maggie. What shall we do? We know not to go near, but it looks so weak. Do you think the mother has deserted it because it's ill?" Mrs. Breck asked nervously.

"How is it behaving?" I asked routinely. "Is it sitting erect or lying prone on its side? Does it cry softly, as though hungry, or sharply, as if in pain? Does it seem ill at ease, or comfortable?"

"Well, we can see the ears twitching. It's not crying. Most of the time it just sleeps. I guess you might say it seems at ease," she answered uncertainly.

"Then let's just try leaving it alone for a while longer," I assured her. "The mother knows where she left her fawn, and she will be back soon to feed it. They usually return at dusk."

Another hour passed before the phone ran again. "Maggie, I don't want to be a nuisance, but the doe hasn't shown up, and we're getting anxious. What if the fawn really is sick and needs help?"

"All right, I'll come over and check it out. It never hurts to be sure. I'll be there in ten minutes."

I stood indoors to view the fawn from the Brecks' window. It appeared to be a fine healthy little animal, curled quietly in a comfortable position and sleeping soundly. I could see no sign of stress. The Brecks agreed to leave the baby undisturbed until after dark. I explained that a doe will wait until all neighboring activities have stopped before coming into a human area, such as their backyard to retrieve her young one.

As the sun retreated behind the western hills, the phone rang once more. "Maggie, you were right. What a treat. The doe is out there this minute nursing her fawn. When she appeared from down in the creek bed, the hungry baby jumped up eagerly. It ran to her side and ducked under her flank for his long awaited dinner." The Brecks were delighted with their front row seat.

Callers often insist that any lone fawn has been abandoned. In my experience with ill or injured deer, this is not the case. In one instance, the rangers at Sugar Loaf State Park heard the constant cries of a newborn fawn. The mother and her fawn of last year grazed in the field where it lay. The rangers hesitated to approach the fawn since the doe seemed to be hovering near.

They watched with concern as the mother walked to the side of the fawn, licked and nudged it, then resumed her grazing while the yearling stood at a distance. At intervals, she continued to circle and nudge the baby, as if to comfort it, as it cried weakly and plaintively. The apparent helplessness of the doe prompted the rangers to notify Fawn Rescue.

At the top of a steep mountain grade I slowed to drive into the park entrance. A park ranger waited to guide me to the broad open field, still a lush and vivid green from the late spring rains. The doe stepped back as I approached with a blanket thrown over my arm. I knelt beside the newborn fawn lying weak and ill in the tall damp grass. The troubled mother watched anxiously as I gently wrapped the baby in a clean, soft blanket, but she made no attempt to interfere or challenge me. It seemed as though she knew that I had come to help. Did some inner connection, an energy between us, assure her and keep her undisturbed and at a distance?

I walked out of the field carrying the tiny bundle in my arms and placed the now silent fawn in a carrier for the drive home. Once there, I cleaned, weighed and examined her. I found no obvious injuries to her body, but she held her head at a strange angle, as though peering into some distant space. Her expression was blank, her eyes dull. That's it, I thought. She's blind.

Later that day my vet, Dr. Patton, confirmed my suspicion. He held little hope that her eyes would respond to treatment, but gave me medication nonetheless. She ate well and gained strength. But once on her feet, she walked slowly in tight circles. Although in a small secure enclosure with very young fawns, she panicked each time she heard a sound. She didn't know where the others ran or why. Several days passed. She became more stressed, remained totally without sight, and finally stopped eating. Plainly her body had shut down. Unable to cope, she would never function as a normal deer and was slowly dying. Sadly, I drove her into Dr. Patton's clinic where we quietly and mercifully put her to sleep.

*

A few weeks later, a fawn old enough to actively follow its mother went through a barbed-wire fence, rather than over it, as the doe had done, and was caught tightly. In response to the rancher's call, I was on the scene within a half hour to rescue the little buck. The doe remained close by, never venturing far from the fence where I struggled to cut the heavy wire and release the now unconscious fawn.

After working its body free, I strapped the badly wounded little deer to my wheeled stretcher. I pulled him to the truck and carefully placed him in the back. Just then the doe walked up close to the truck, glanced at her fawn, then looked directly at me, as if to ask where her fawn would go. I lifted the tailgate, closing the small injured animal in.

How I wished to somehow be able to communicate with the distressed mother to assure her that I'd make her baby well and return him to her. As I drove off, the doe followed behind, then ran alongside the truck. Finally, as I rounded a sharp bend in the dirt road, she bounded off into the thicket with her other fawn running by her side. While driving toward the vet clinic, I found comfort in knowing she still had one baby to nurture.

Two weeks later, forty stitches in the small buck's right leg were removed by the always willing Dr. Patton. Within days, I drove the fully recovered fawn, anxious for freedom, to the trail where his mother and sibling had last been seen. He leaped out without hesitation through the open door of the truck and disappeared into his familiar wild world.

It has been my experience that wild mothers don't abandon their offspring in times of sickness or trouble, and once reunited, they eagerly accept them back in spite of any human involvement.

7

Pequeño - Little Male

The old man had lived alone since the death of his wife four years ago. He still took pride in keeping her cherished flower beds in perfect order. Each evening, after completing his farm chores, he devoted a few minutes to weeding and watering. He listened contentedly to the pervasive hum of the bees circling and pollinating his blossoming Gravenstein apples and Santa Rosa plums which grew alongside rows of massive walnut trees.

His satisfaction peaked as his wandering gaze swept across the wide valley below. His eyes paused on the jagged, dark green edges of Sonoma Mountain to the west. As he stood dreaming, contented with life, Ben Statler glanced down from his hillside vantage point in time to glimpse two men lift a small spotted fawn from their pickup and carry it toward their house. Suddenly the door burst open and three excited children danced and squealed as one of the men placed the fawn in their eager outstretched hands. The men stood back and laughed at their antics.

That night the mild weather turned cold again, and for several weeks Ben saw little activity in the house below. He watched from his window that overlooked the Sonoma Valley, searching for some sign of the fawn. Seeing none, he hoped the family had been instructed by the ranch owner for whom they worked to turn the fawn over to the proper authorities. However, his hopes were soon shattered. One warm morning while watering his garden, he noticed a child carry a bottle out to a wooden crate in back of the house. When a tiny brown head appeared, the young boy pushed the nipple into the animal's mouth. So the fawn has been raised indoors as a pet all these weeks, and now that it's getting too big for the house it's been put in a crate. I'm glad to see it's still alive at any rate, he thought, as he put down the watering hose. I hate to interfere in someone else's business, but I'd better call Art Faulkner to find out if he's aware of this.

Ben returned indoors to put in his call to the neighboring ranch owner. After identifying himself and voicing his concern, he added, "I realize theirs is a different culture, and they see no harm in what they're doing, but you and I both know this is against the law, and for good reason."

Faulkner replied curtly that he wasn't interested in a fawn. "I don't intend to interfere. They're doing their job, and that's what I pay them for. If it's against the law, it doesn't concern me one way or the other." Faulkner slammed down the phone in the ear of the troubled old man.

Days passed as Ben continued to observe the tightly confined fawn laying lethargically in the crate. With so little space to move in, it rarely stood except when being fed. Ben thought back to when it had arrived and how old it might have been then. Perhaps a week old, very tiny. It must be six or eight weeks old by now, he calculated. "No exercise, just milk," he mumbled. "It should be eating solid food by now, like one of my calves would be. This is a bad situation. Tomorrow I'll walk down to talk to the family."

After breakfast the following morning, Ben picked up his walking stick and headed down the hillside path toward the ranch worker's living quarters. He knocked on the door of the third house. He spoke no Spanish, but since the family spoke and understood a limited amount of English, he managed to let them know of his concern for the small caged fawn. They walked outside with him, pointed to the captive, and explained that this was Pequeño, which means little male. Pequeño belonged to the children, they said. They kept him in the crate so that he wouldn't run away, they explained. They smiled politely, but didn't budge in their determination to keep the fawn.

The old man slowly and reluctantly climbed the hill toward home feeling defeated, but not willing to give up his intention to change the fawn's life threatening situation. Tomorrow I'll find out who to contact. Probably Animal Control. No, it's a weekend. They'll be closed. Well, I guess it will just have to wait until Monday, he concluded, as he halted on the trail for breath.

The next day Ben got up early before the heat to chop weeds along the edge of the hillside. The cloudless sky and brilliant sun gave promise of a hot day. The children below played ball while the fawn languished in the crate. Suddenly the shrill bleat of an animal caught his attention. As Ben looked in the direction of the disturbance, a thin dark haired woman appeared around the corner of the house struggling with a heavy crate containing the fawn. As he continued to watch from his hillside vantage point, she dragged it across the road, lifted the fawn out of the crate, and dropped it into a small tightly fenced field located across the driveway from the house. He heard the high questioning voices of the children, who crowded around their mother. He understood from the woman's gestures that the fawn would now live in the field, since it had grown too large for the crate. She returned to the house, then reappeared with a bottle, which she handed to the oldest child. Ben watched as the fawn drank and then lay down against the fence. So the woman did understand my concern for the fawn living in that small crate and decided to take action. Good for her, he thought. But this is still not the answer. There's no shade, no food, and no water in that barren field. The animal looks so thin. It will die. It can't possibly survive long in this heat, he worried.

Monday morning the fawn could be seen from Ben's window, still lying listlessly against the fence next to the road, obviously watching for a child to bring the milk that was its only source of nourishment. The field had been mowed several weeks ago, and now it contained nothing but dry, brittle, brown stubble, which a deer cannot eat.

Placing his coffee cup on the sink counter, Ben walked to the phone and put in a call to Animal Control to voice his complaint. The operator transferred his call to Fawn Rescue. As I listened, Ben once again explained his concern for Pequeño. He urged me to act quickly. "The fawn won't live another day in this heat without shade or water," he said.

"I'm concerned, too, Mr. Statler, but Pequeño is on private property, and I can't just walk in and pick him up, as much as I'd like to. This problem must be handled through the Department of Fish and Game. I'll try to find a warden to go with me. It may take some time. At this time of day, they're out in the field, and aren't always available. I'll get back to you as soon as I know when I'll be picking up the fawn." I immediately dialed dispatch at the Department's headquarters.

"Maggie, as usual, they are all gone. There isn't a warden working anywhere near Sonoma. It will be hours before one can get to you, but I'll keep trying to find help," the dispatch operator promised. In the meantime, as I waited, feeling frustrated by my inability to rescue the fawn alone, I decided to call our County Patrol Warden and leave a message for him at home. To my surprise, he was there, recovering from surgery and happy for some diversion. He promised to contact a warden to confiscate the fawn.

Within an hour, a call came through from Warden Sue Lang. "Maggie, give me the address where that fawn is being held. I'll bring another warden with me and meet you at the gate. Several of us are here at the hatchery, so someone should be available. We can be there in forty-five minutes." I hung up and dialed Ben's number, knowing he would be waiting anxiously for news.

The two wardens waited by the road to the entrance of the Faulkner property. Dick Kendall said he and Sue didn't see the fawn in the field. "Ben said it lies close against the fence. He's never seen it out in the field," I explained. I swung my little pickup in behind the Department's truck, and we traveled slowly up the narrow road, carefully watching for Pequeño. Suddenly Dick slowed to a stop and pointed out his window toward the field. Pulling our trucks to the side of the drive, we could plainly see the fawn curled up in the stubble with the late afternoon sun blazing down on his back. The little buck never lifted his head as we stepped from our vehicles and moved toward him with caution.

"He looks in bad shape," whispered Sue, as she made ready to climb over the wire fence to retrieve him. "We'd better get him out of that heat first, then find the house where the family lives. We'll talk to them once the fawn is safe."

"Here," I said, handing Sue a bottle of water. "He should come right to you when he sees the bottle."

Once she entered the field, Sue crouched and slowly approached the now alert fawn. As anticipated, Pequeño had long ago lost all fear of humans and ran eagerly toward her, his eyes focused intently on the bottle. As he began to suck, Sue reached forward to grab him. He backed away and ran a few feet into the field. "Try holding the bottle firmly with one hand, then reach around the back of his neck with the other hand so he doesn't see it coming," I suggested from outside the fence. "Once you get a grip on his neck, push down. As he flattens himself on the ground, straddle him quickly. You won't get a second chance," I warned.

This time the warden got Pequeño firmly under her control. Dick grabbed the blanket I threw him and jumped over the fence to give her a hand with the struggling, screaming animal. Sue climbed over the fence and turned to reach for the tightly wrapped fawn as Dick handed him over. As she placed him in the Fawnmobile, a woman came running from the house with a small boy trailing behind her. "Pequeño! Pequeño!" she screamed. She then shouted to us, "What are you doing to our baby deer?"

I approached her to explain that this was the Department of Fish and Game. We had received a call to rescue the fawn. The distraught woman replied, "No, no. You can't have the little deer. He belongs to the children. He is ours. You are hurting him."

I tried to make her see how very ill the fawn appeared to be. "Look at him," I said. "He's so thin and his hair is dry and dull. He hasn't had the right food or enough water. He needs lots of greens and grain to grow strong." I continued to explain, trying hard to get through to her. "See how weak he is? He had no exercise in the crate. There's no shade or water in the field. Please try to understand. He'll die in this heat. Besides, Pequeño needs to be with other fawns. Tonight he'll be sleeping with little deer just his age. You see how much better that will be for him?"

"No. There's nothing wrong with Pequeño. He's fine and you can't have him," she insisted and took a step in the direction of the Fawnmobile.

The warden stepped up beside me to suggest that I leave with the fawn. He said he and Sue would stay to explain the law to the woman and why the fawn was in need of help. Usually the Department doesn't issue a citation to the public for a first offense. I left with the hope that the woman and her child would understand.

Pequeño was isolated for his first two days, as are all newcomers at Fawn Rescue and showed no sign of any illness that could contaminate another fawn. He contentedly lay in the shade of a large toyon bush where he could reach for a succulent leaf without stirring. He devoured acorns and oak leaves, poison oak, vetch and wild grape leaves—all the luscious greens that were so new and natural to him. He showed no further interest in the bottle, preferring grain and the variety of vegetation he found in abundance in his pen.

Shortly before Pequeño arrived, I had accepted a fawn with a pelvic injury from Shasta County where it would have been kept alone. The wildlife organization there had released their last fawn some weeks before and were actively seeking a companion for their late arrival. Organizations have learned that these animals are better prepared for life in the wild if they are raised with their own species. Since Fawn Rescue always seems to have fawns late into the fall, we felt the Shasta fawn, already wild, would have a better chance to retain her wild ways with us.

Pequeño and Shasta, male and female, welcomed each other gladly at the end of his isolation period. Shasta's pelvic injury healed well. Now she needed exercise and nourishment to rebuild her strength. Pequeño, having been denied any association with other deer, contentedly attached himself closely to her. The contact was especially beneficial for him since Shasta had been raised in the wild by her mother. From her, he learned to listen and watch, to dash to the other end of their long enclosure and vanish into the brush at any unusual sound. By late fall, the young buck had gained weight and his new coat of hair grew thick and sleek. Shasta jumped, ran and displayed in every way her readiness to return to the wild. By now both were weaned, their spots had vanished, and their time for release together had come.

One crisp fall morning the young buck and doe were loaded into the Fawnmobile for the drive north to the fifteen-hundred-acre preserve that would be their permanent home. John Erwin, the only resident in this wilderness, called frequently to report on the fawns' progress. For the first several days they stayed close to the release site, he said. They browsed and bedded down in a not-too-distant meadow, always together.

A resident herd of deer made an appearance each day to travel along a well-worn trail down the mountainside, through the meadow, and on to a rushing stream below. Habitually, the group stopped to browse in this lush meadow as they rambled through. At first Pequeño and Shasta stood quietly watching the herd wander past. Wild fawns, belonging to the herd, stopped one day to touch noses and acquaint themselves with the newcomers.

But they were rejected by the does and yearlings who chased them if they came too close. Each evening, as the herd made its way down to the stream, the two cautious juveniles began to follow at a safe distance. Finally, the property owner called me to say that after many weeks of patient following, Pequeño and Shasta gained acceptance from the group.

During their second season on the refuge, John delighted in identifying them by their small ear tags flashing in the sun. The two yearlings browsed and wandered with their chosen family over the mountain top, across the meadow and down the well-worn path to the stream.

8
Of Dogs and Deer

Fawn Rescue receives many fawns each year that are seriously injured due to dog attacks while others die unaided in remote areas. The true count of wildlife brought down by unrestrained domestic animals will never be known.

The tragedy is that wildlife continues to be chased, captured, and killed by family pets that are allowed undisciplined freedom. Often dogs that are confined by day go on a rampage of destruction for fun and exercise when they are released after dark. Their canine instinct urges them to group into packs of overly energetic predators. They incite each other into acts not otherwise expected of gentle family companions. Even the most loving pet can become dangerous after picking up a strange scent or catching the quick movement of a wild animal running across an open field.

Many times these incidents are witnessed by humans so there can be no doubt the dog is responsible. After the chase, the dog quickly loses interest, abandons the dead or mortally wounded animal, and dashes off to new adventures. This aggressive behavior, if encouraged or fortified, instills in the dog an underlying sense that this is acceptable behavior. This urge to kill may be transferred from wildlife to home life, and future prey may be a domestic animal or even a child. There are few natural predators still at large that can bring down a fleet-footed fawn, and unlike a dog, a wild predator kills for the food it needs to survive.

Although, at times, the injuries are only superficial, yet the fawn usually dies. These delicate creatures cannot cope with the terror of the frenzied chase and capture. The inability to escape forces these innocent wild ones into shock, which is nature's way of providing wildlife with a means of escape from a painful and horrifying death. The public is generally unaware of the tragic circumstances under which Fawn Rescue receives these calls for help.

One morning a small fawn and a doe crossed the path of a dog whose owner had, only minutes before, removed the restraining leash to allow their pet some freedom. Immediately, the dog chased and caught the fawn, then attacked the doe when she tried to intervene. The badly mauled fawn, its hind leg broken, tried to escape. As the owner watched in horror, the small animal rolled down a steep embankment. Too late, the owner restrained the excited dog and carried the injured fawn to her car. In order to protect their pet, the family didn't consult a vet. At home, they dressed the fawn's wounds and made an attempt to set the broken bones. This family, inexperienced in dealing with wildlife, fed the injured animal cow's milk, a deadly diet for a fawn. Two days later, when the fawn appeared to be dying, the dog's owner urgently called Fawn Rescue. Beyond help, the fawn died on the way to a vet. This well meaning, but uninformed family didn't anticipate these tragic consequences from their walk in the woods.

*

Even those times when the intent of the dog is harmless, it can inflict great damage on a young wild animal. One family's gentle collie suddenly became extremely protective of its kennel, allowing no one near. Two days of this unusual behavior led the owner to discover a newborn fawn hidden in the far rear corner of the doghouse. The dog had instinctively replaced her recently lost pups. The owner's quick action prevented the fawn from dying of starvation.

Nonetheless, this free-roaming collie was responsible for the fawn being separated from its mother and nearly paying with its life. One week later, the owner found the same dog harboring a second fawn. Due to an immediate call to Fawn Rescue from the highly embarrassed dog owner, both fawns recovered and were eventually released far from humanity. This collie is now confined to a large fenced yard. Few dog-related incidents have such successful endings.

*

A man called to report that he recognized a neighbor's Golden Retriever trotting along a country road with a newborn fawn dangling upside down from its mouth. The man stopped his car to coax the dog to give up its prey. The well trained retriever dragged the fawn by its hind leg and dropped it as ordered. The fawn, caught from behind, had its hind quarters crushed beyond repair. I drove many miles through back roads with this badly mangled little buck cradled beside me, only to reach the closest vet clinic too late for it to be helped.

*

One spring day a hiker stopped to talk to a young woman as she sat in the tall grass on the side of a hill. They discussed the beauty of the surrounding wilderness area and the promise of a lovely day. As they spoke, a deadly scream broke the tranquility.

"What's that?" asked the startled young man.

"Oh, my dog must be running something down again," the woman casually replied. "He loves these chases on our walks. Good exercise. Some of the animals are pretty fast."

Not waiting to hear more, the hiker dashed up the side of the embankment to disappear over the hill. In an open field he found the dog growling and shaking a fawn by its neck. The screaming had stopped. The doe lay dead beside them. As the man, crying out in rage, sped towards the alarmed dog, it dropped the fawn and headed in the direction of its mistress.

The young man gently carried the cold, wet, dying fawn down to the road. The woman and her dog had gone. He ran to the nearest farm to call for help, but it was too late. As he spoke to me on the phone, the small wild creature died in his arms. The horrified hiker vowed to trace the ownership of the dog and make a detailed report to the county Animal Regulation Department.

Squirrels, hares, raccoons, birds—all wildlife—are prey to unrestrained domestic animals. Each of us must take responsibility for our pets, keeping them under control as the law requires. These laws are essential to the welfare of wildlife whose lives are at risk. Enjoy them while they still share our beautiful land.

9
Mindless Decisions

Human callousness, ignorance, and indifference are responsible for the deaths of countless numbers of wildlife. The animals, so wantonly destroyed, are not lesser but equal, and in some senses, superior to man. Mountain lions and brush rabbits, bears and reptiles, coyotes, eagles and earthworms, all of earth's creatures, far too many near the brink of extinction, are all individually valuable contributors to the delicate balance of nature.

As I recall two particularly senseless incidents, I remain filled with both rage and a deep sadness. They continue to haunt me.

Humans are enchanted with the innocent, fragile beauty of fawns. Yet, because of this strong attraction, these appealing young ones die needlessly each year. In one instance, the Jenkins family could not resist picking up a small fawn they found in a park. They brought it home with the intention of having a "family experience" in raising it, they said. Teaching their children to ignore the law set the first in a series of bad examples. Acknowledging no difference between domestic animals and wildlife was another.

During my rescues I learn of some incredible diets offered these small, still nursing, wild herbivores. People thoughtlessly place before them, and expect them to eat, dog food, buttermilk, raw eggs, and any left-overs they would otherwise throw to their dogs. No thought is given to the age or needs of the species. The Jenkins family fed their captive fawn diluted evaporated milk, which promptly resulted in diarrhea and dehydration. Not knowing how to deal with the sick newborn, Mrs. Jenkins left an urgent message on the Fawn Rescue answering machine. I responded at once and listened to her answers to my questions.

"I'm glad you called so quickly, Mrs. Jenkins. The food you're giving it has no strength to sustain it for even another day. It needs a much richer diet," I explained. "You're right to be concerned. This fawn is in danger of dying. I'll pick it up at once and get it back on the road to health."

"All I want to know from you is what to feed it," she responded angrily. "I'm not giving you the fawn."

"But you can't buy the proper diet," I told her. "Our formula is made especially for fawns. It's not for sale to the public because of the law that forbids holding wildlife in captivity and raising them as pets."

"I know the law," she answered with stinging sharpness. "We live so far out in the valley that no one will ever know we have it. We want the children to have the fun and experience of raising a wild animal. However, if you're not willing to help us, we'll manage without your formula."

"Wait," I said quickly to prevent her from hanging up. Then I gave her my most compelling argument against keeping it. "You surely don't want your children to watch the fawn die and know that you are responsible for its death, do you?" Little did I know, just then, how prophetic these words would be.

From the background, her husband's voice came through clearly over the phone, urging her to hang up. "Hold on a minute," she said. "I'm putting my husband on the other line."

With both parents on the phone, I desperately tried to convince them to allow me to pick up the fawn before dark. I used every conceivable argument in an attempt to persuade them to relinquish the sick young animal, stressing the danger of delaying treatment any longer.

"No. You can't come up tonight," he replied. "We're going to bed soon. We have to be in Novato early tomorrow morning."

"Oh, then that will work out fine. You'll drive right through Santa Rosa, and I can meet you wherever you say, and at any time," I offered. Assuming they would agree, I continued, "Just don't feed it any more evaporated milk tonight. It won't hurt it to go without one meal."

"We're not planning to bring the fawn to you," he cut in coldly. "I thought my wife made it clear to you that we're keeping it."

Before giving me a chance to reply, Mrs. Jenkins broke into the conversation to say, "We've heard all of your arguments. We'll discuss it tonight and let you know in the morning. We understand what you're saying, but this is a family decision."

"No, there's no decision to make," I stated firmly. "The fawn is dying. You called me knowing it needs help, and I promise you it will have the best care possible. It will be raised with other fawns and be well prepared to take its place in the wild. I can't see why you object to turning this ill fawn over to me."

"Because it's our fawn, and we'll decide what's best for it," she answered with venom in her voice.

Totally frustrated by this couple's lack of concern for the welfare of the sick fawn, I could not allow the conversation to finish on that note. "No, it's not your fawn. Wildlife belongs to no one. Please don't let this one die needlessly," I begged.

"We heard you. There's nothing more to discuss," she finished abruptly as they both hung up their phone receivers.

I waited until ten o'clock the following morning before admitting that the Jenkinses didn't intend to call. I reluctantly reported the incident to the Department of Fish and Game and requested their help in rescuing the fawn.

In response to my call, Warden Sam Holland tried to contact Mrs. Jenkins often throughout the day without success. That evening I received his report. "Maggie, there is no fawn," his sober voice informed me.

"What? I don't understand, Sam. What happened?" I asked filled with dread.

"The Jenkins family has a group of deer that travel through their back acreage. They decided to just put the fawn out as the herd wandered by," he began.

"Oh, no, surely not. How could they be sure there was a lactating mother in the group? How could they be sure a strange doe would adopt a baby not her own? That fawn will starve," I protested. "Mrs. Jenkins never called to ask if that would be a safe procedure. I could have told her that in the deer family, a doe will reject any fawn that isn't her own. I would have warned her that they force any newcomer out of the herd. Did she check with the Department, Sam?"

"She didn't. This was a family decision, she told me. But let me finish. That's not the whole story, I'm afraid."

"What else? I don't think I want to hear more."

"Mrs. Jenkins very calmly told me that they put the fawn out on the edge of the field. The fawn ran away from them, and their dog caught it and killed it. The whole family stood helplessly by and watched."

"No. No. That fawn didn't need to die, and so violently. If they had just let me have it last night, it would still be alive. If they were willing to just dump it out, not knowing its fate, why wouldn't they let me have it?"

"I don't know what tempts people to make the choices they do, Maggie. I'm so very sorry. I didn't see the fawn in their possession, so I couldn't even give them a citation. Not a thing I could do."

Still, I wonder. When the resident deer herd gathers each day at sundown to graze in the distant field gleaming as gold as a spotted fawn, does a sharp sting of conscience reach deep into their psyche to touch a tender nerve?

*

A well meaning, but uninformed young couple watched, night after night, as a doe's alert and healthy two-month-old fawn followed her across the highway in front of their rural home. For generations, deer herds journeyed down this well-established path that led from a gently sloping hillside covered with browse down to the banks of a deep, clear rushing stream. Although a road now cut through this ancient trail, the deer, having no concept of vehicles or of their potential danger to them, continued to cross to the opposite side for water.

After several anxious nights worrying that the fawn would be hit by an oncoming car, the Fullers decided that this doe was not teaching her fawn safe habits, and, therefore, she was not a responsible mother. So, like a social worker assigned to take charge in a child neglect case, they felt the responsibility to take action.

Once this foolish notion had become firmly established in their minds, their next thought was to rescue the fawn and raise it where it could grow up out of harm's way. It never occurred to these two young people that this could be a nursing fawn, or that it might already be imprinted with wildlife's instinctive fear of man.

Once the decision had been made, action followed quickly. The Fullers invited another couple to participate in the interception of the fawn as it crossed to the stream the following evening at dusk. The friends chased the frightened creature into the corner of a field-fence boarding the road and captured it. The doe, crossing ahead of the fawn, had vanished into the brush, which, to the Fullers, only reinforced their strongly held opinion that she was a negligent mother.

The frantic fawn screamed, kicked and fought for its freedom, but was subdued by the rescue party. Elated by their success on the first try, they struggled to carry the terrified young animal into their strongly fenced back yard. They placed a bucket of water in the corner, closed the gate securely, and left it to calm down for the night. The wild, captured fawn threw itself repeatedly into the chain link fence trying to escape and join its mother on the other side.

Early the next morning, the Fullers were appalled to discover the fawn lying prone, in shock, bleeding from the mouth, with multiple abrasions covering its small body. Fawn Rescue received a desperate, urgent call for help, to which I responded at once. At the vet clinic X-rays revealed the broken neck. The devastated, contrite young couple had a difficult time coping with the news that the completely paralyzed fawn had been mercifully euthanized. They became strong advocates for wildlife education, especially in circulating the message to let wildlife live as nature intended, without human interference.

10

Squirrels I Have Known

Two species of tree squirrels are native to Sonoma County, in addition to the California Ground squirrel. The Western Gray squirrel is large, silver-gray with a white underside and a spectacular busy tail.

The Douglas Chickaree is relatively small with a gleaming chestnut back, white belly and a distinctive black stripe running between its upper and lower sides. The Douglas Chickaree is native to remote coniferous forests and is seldom seen. Therefore, it is essential to their survival that they be returned to their own limited habitat when they are ready for release.

In contrast, the Western Grays live throughout the county and are most familiar to the public and to wildlife care givers. Many Western Gray squirrels of all ages pass through the Fawn Rescue facility and have become another of our specialties.

One particularly busy season, one family's cat caught a finger-length newborn gray squirrel, her eyes still closed, ears sealed and a body pink and bare as a salamander. She was entered in our log book as squirrel "number three." Totally dependent, she thrived on her every three-hour feedings around the clock. As she grew, she graduated from her snug bed of soft cloth to a large outdoor cage in our oak woods where she developed the skills she needed to survive in the wild.

She was approximately ten-weeks old when I opened the gate to her cage, and the young squirrel named Three scampered high into a nearby oak. Instinctively she began gathering twigs, bark and moss for nest building. Newly released squirrels are seldom seen again, but to our delight, Three decided to settle in close to the place where she had been raised. Although she often leaped down from an overhanging madrone tree to visit, she remained completely wild, never permitting us to touch her. Taking one small step too close would cause her to spring away, scold and stamp her foot at us in reprimand.

During the spring of her second year, and each spring thereafter, Three produced a litter of offspring, but, strangely, she never brought them down to visit us. One wet season, as she diligently rounded up material to use in preparing a nest, we watched her numerous trips in the direction of our hanging plants. She emerged with long strands of macrame jute dangling from the corners of her overloaded mouth like a handle-bar mustache. She cropped the jute so close to the underside of the pots that the weight broke the weakened hangers, sending the plants crashing onto the deck.

Large deck pots filled with vividly colored annuals became her favorite digging and burying spots. Potting soil and plants flew in every direction as her treasures were pushed deep into the soft mulch. Soon nothing remained in the pots but soil and mounds of walnuts. I tolerated her destructive behavior, replanting time after time.

As fall settled in, the walnuts we gathered were spread to dry. Three spent hours each day boldly helping herself from the drying racks filled with the tasty treats being readied for storage. Next spring these nuts would be needed for baby squirrel diets. She fanatically craved the soft succulent meat of the newly harvested nuts. We never tired watching her as she expertly twirled and checked each nut before flitting off into the woods with her prize or purposefully heading in the direction of my potted plants. We permitted her to carry away as many as she wished, since her share amounted to only a small portion of the total crop.

Often the sound of her hearty bound across the roof distracted me. Glancing up from my desk I saw Three balancing on her back legs, peering through the window. Even before I laid down my pen, she scampered across the deck to wait at the bird feeding platform for her nuts.

In her later years Three developed a summer allergy which left her with raw patches on her skin from the constant scratching. We had the means to help, but were unable to capture her for treatment. She refused any food containing medication no matter how subtle the taste or smell. As fall approached, the rash disappeared and her skin healed quickly.

During her last year we could see Three aging. Her tail hair thinned until it no longer provided her with protection from inclement winter weather. Unable to leap from tree to tree, she scurried along an arboreal path of tightly growing branches. We mentally prepared ourselves to accept our pending loss, but, nevertheless, when she failed to return during one particularly cold wet spell, we anxiously watched for weeks before finally conceding that she had died. This dearly loved, delightful wild creature gave us joy for nine long rewarding years. The rare privilege of her companionship remains as an unforgettable part of our lives.

*

Sometimes squirrels that are released at Fawn Rescue quickly disappear, never to be seen again, but either by coincidence or by fate, Miwok came to live at our facility the same month that Three died. Her decision to make our grove her permanent home after her release helped lessen our sorrow over the loss of our resident squirrel of so many years. A doctor and his family who found this newborn lying helpless and cold under the mighty fir tree from which she had fallen, delivered her to me in an Easter basked filled with soft tissue.

As I carefully lifted her out of the basket, her right hind leg twisted oddly under her body. Our vet, Dr. Patton, performed his usual miracles on the infinitely small and fragile bones of this finger-sized squirrel. He inserted a miniature pin to hold the fractured bones together and provided medication to prevent infection. Within weeks this tiny determined creature began to explore the logs and branches that were placed in her cage to encourage her to exercise and strengthen her rapidly developing body.

Miwok's leg healed straight and strong. At twelve weeks of age she began pacing the perimeter of her cage indicating her need to be free. The rains of spring had stopped. Pale yellow growth appeared on the ends of the oak branches. Mushrooms pushed up from beneath the forest mulch, sending their musky fragrance as an enticement for the wild creatures who searched for the succulent fresh growth of the season. The time was right for this anxious wild one to go out into her squirrel world.

Once free, Miwok immediately gathered nesting material, just as Three had done. She settled in a nearby thick stand of trees which provided her with a protective cover from the soaring and ever searching hawks.

One day I glanced out to see an old familiar sight: uprooted plants and potting soil were flung in abandon on one corner of the deck while flower pots were filled with stored treasures — tell-tale signs of our resident squirrel. Not again, I thought. This time I decided to take quick action. I placed small mesh wire over the soil in the pots, which allowed the plants to grow up through the wire. This put an immediate halt to Miwok's destructive behavior. She soon learned that she had the entire forest for her storage area, but my plants were off limits.

As I write, Miwok is just over one year old. She remains independent and free, an important addition to the wild creatures that make our land their home.

*

I recently rescued an alert adult female gray squirrel that had been brushed by a car. At Dr. Patton's vet clinic she fought in protest against the injection of steroids given to her for head trauma. Luckily, we found no bleeding or broken bones.

In our large outdoor cage, in a cool wooded section of Fawn Rescue, she began her long convalescence. Each day I quietly observed her from a distance, approaching only to replenish her food or freshen her water.

On her fifth day in captivity she gave birth to a 12.73-gram, two-inch-long male and a stillborn female. Only partially recovered, this mother remained far too ill to nurture her baby. She settled high on a shelf, far from her newborn, and seemed totally unaware of his needs. Cautiously entering the cage, I picked up the barely alive, cold and clammy baby and cupped it against my neck to provide warmth. The ill mother continued to lie exhausted on her perch, unmindful of my entry and the removal of her offspring. As I ran up the path to the house, his tiny cold body slowly drew warmth from mine. Once inside, I cleaned his finger-sized body and weighed him on my gram scale. Then, judging from his weight, I fed him a very small portion of squirrel formula with a miniature syringe. When he stirred, I knew he was well on his way to an eventful squirrel life.

Intrigued by this unique experience, and grateful for the opportunity to observe the growth of a newborn squirrel from its first minute of birth, I kept meticulous records of each gram of increased weight, each millimeter of food consumed, and each new pattern of development. Spellbound, I watched as tiny dots on either side of his head peaked into recognizable ears. Eye slits appeared in the blue bulges that would one day open to view his squirrel world. Whiskers, barely discernible, sprouted from his hairless cheeks. Pads formed on the underside of his paws. Dark nails, as small as a grain of sand, grew from the end of each toe, as dot thumbs emerged above them. And, finally, at the end of this perfect miniature body, a toothpick tail curled tightly under his legs.

Two weeks later this thriving squirrel's button nose became more prominent, and two sharp bottom incisors pushed through his gums. Gradually, pale gray down covered his rapidly growing pink body. One morning I picked him up for his early meal to find one dark inquiring eye open. By evening both shining orbs followed me alertly as I walked close to his bed box. During this eventful fourth week of life his ears unsealed, and two top incisors emerged.

Each day the mother squirrel became more active and eventually recovered completely from her injuries. One sunny morning before breakfast, I swung her cage door open wide. She made one frantic leap over my shoulder and disappeared forever into the trees.

As her young one grows, I marvel that this awesome creature, born with pink transparent skin, blue bulging eye protrusions and long naked limbs, will one day be prepared to take his place in our natural world.

*

Not all squirrels brought to Fawn Rescue for care are released directly from their cages onto our acreage. Some are transported to other private, protected land where they remain safe from human interference and danger. I prefer to keep those with special problems close by to be sure they have adjusted well to the wild, although one has never needed to be recaptured.

At the tender age of five weeks squirrels emerge from the security of their nests, called drays. As these youngsters scamper, learning their squirrel skills, they sometimes lose their grip on the high overhead branches and fall many feet to the ground. A dray is a tunnel structure, twelve to sixteen inches deep, having a side entrance. Built twenty to sixty feet off the ground, often in the crotch of a tree, it consists of woven branches and twigs. The cavity is lined with shredded moss, grass and ferns. Twigs and leaves are anchored over all as waterproofing.

These fragile structures are vulnerable to heavy storms. Strong winds topple them to the ground, tree trimmers bring them crashing earthward, sometimes inadvertently spewing infant squirrels in every direction. These babies, prey to any nearby predator, are often rescued from the mouth of a pet and delivered to our facility.

As with fawns, to distinguish between these look-alike creatures, I give them descriptive names. Three Toes was one such squirrel. Three Toes had been caught, tossed and mangled by a large dog. Her siblings were killed before the owner could get close. This small female was rescued from a similar fate and taken into the dog owner's home. As often happens, the family attempted to treat and feed her.

Several days of unsuccessful effort finally led them to seek help from Fawn Rescue. When I first saw this infant squirrel's condition, I held little hope for her survival. Nevertheless, I rushed her to Dr. Patton for X-rays and an examination which revealed two broken ribs and neurological damage to two toes of her right front paw. This paw, swollen to three times its normal size, looked as though it were encased in a baseball glove. An infected cornea rendered her right eye sightless, and a deep laceration under her chin needed immediate stitching. A large spot of fur torn from her back would take considerable time to heal. In addition to all these injuries, Three Toes suffered from diarrhea and dehydration due to improper diet. Dr. Patton warned me of this badly mauled squirrel's slim chance for recovery, but since she had somehow managed to survive this far, she deserved that chance, no matter how slim.

After days of antibiotic injections, ophthalmic drops to heal the cornea, then removal of the scar tissue from her eye, her sight returned. Three Toes showed miraculous signs of rapid improvement. She learned to adapt well to the loss of all but three of her five toes. Many weeks of proper nourishment, rest, and plenty of TLC finally resulted in the day this little girl squirrel went on her way, joyfully swinging through the trees.

*

I vividly recall the day I drove over the mountain to Napa to pick up a fully grown squirrel that had been injured under unusual circumstances. Betty Donner had become deeply attached to Pomo after finding him, while still a baby, lying helpless on her patio. The giant Douglas fir tree, from which he had fallen, dominated her front yard. At that time the young squirrel suffered from a noticeable injury to one hind leg, but since he managed to compensate quite well, the woman decided he didn't need professional help.

So many times, as this case represents, the individual who rescues a wild baby cannot bear to part with the appealing creature. Although they have no training in the animal's care, nor any knowledge of their special needs, they decide to raise the animal themselves in spite of the law forbidding this practice. This specific law was not written to deprive the public of the pleasure of raising wildlife, but to protect the animal or bird from the variety of risks it encounters in this type of situation. Wildlife raised as domestic pets, fed unnatural diets, and imprinted to human ways, have not acquired the skills necessary to cope in a wild environment. Once they have grown past infancy these creatures, born wild, become aggressive, demand their freedom, and do not make good pets.

Pomo, raised indoors in a small cage for several months, had been well fed, although not properly fed. As a consequence, he became malnourished, his bones grew fragile, and his muscles grew weak. He had no strength to grip with his long thinly-developed nails. Therefore, on the day he was set free, he fell back onto Miss Donner's paved patio once more. This time the brittle bones on both back legs shattered. Finally, in defeat, Miss Donner called Fawn Rescue for help.

I found the home to be located on a busy, populated city street. Traffic rolled by at a steady pace. The fir tree, from which Pomo fell, covered her small yard well. Squirrels from a nearby park were enticed by the many cones that lay scattered beneath the tree and hung in abundance from every branch. Although her home was not ideal wildlife habitat, Miss Donner insisted that Pomo must be returned to her yard when he recovered. Anxious to get the suffering squirrel to the vet for treatment, I left without fully convincing her that Pomo's future home must be one that would provide a safer environment.

X-rays showed fractures to both tibias. Dr. Patton inserted minute pins into each leg to hold the brittle bones in place while they healed. He cautioned me that Pomo's fragile bones could snap easily, so he must be confined to a limited area until his body had time to grow strong. It would be a long convalescence. We hoped that proper nourishment and rest would give Pomo the opportunity to overcome these serious physical handicaps.

As he slowly recovered, Pomo made little attempt to walk. He put weight on his paws gingerly, as though in pain. Upon checking closely, I discovered his tiny nails had grown into spidery, nearly invisible threads, which made it impossible for him to walk, climb, or cling in a normal squirrel fashion. Over his strong objections, I clipped the outgrowth on each nail. With proper diet his nails grew hard, and this little male began to climb, jump, and fling himself around the cage with glee.

Pomo spent the winter months in a large four-foot indoor cage in a room separate from our living quarters. Finally, as the weather mellowed into balmy spring days, he moved into the outdoor squirrel enclosure, where he enthusiastically began his real body-building exercise. His muscles grew firm, and his hair took on a healthy sheen.

Eventually, as an adult fully prepared for his life as a wild squirrel, Pomo had no further need to live in captivity. Miss Donner was not pleased to be notified that Pomo would be released, not in her city yard, but in a natural squirrel environment. Now, months after his release, he peers down from a lofty branch high overhead, stamps his foot, chatters and scolds, as his dark eyes gleam with contentment.

*

A prominent Northern California attorney, Broderick Harmon, notorious for his heavy drinking and carousing, agreed to accept a unique case involving a street person and a non-native squirrel. Harmon's prestigious clients of years past had grown sparse as his unreliability grew. So in his waning years, he began to rely on the publicity derived from accepting bizarre cases.

When presented with this case, Harmon had no knowledge of wildlife, their needs or habits, and displayed no particular interest in their welfare. But since this case involved a lawsuit against the Department of Fish and Game, which would attract the media and catch the public interest, he willingly agreed to handle it for a nominal fee.

An Eastern Gray squirrel, captured as a juvenile, eventually came into the possession of a panhandler, Mickey Lach, who frequented bars and wandered the streets of San Jose. To maintain control of this captive squirrel, Mickey attached tiny bands to his front legs and secured the bands together with a leather strap. Mickey soon discovered to his delight that the hobbled squirrel, forced to ride on its owner's broad shoulder during their rounds, brought his daily total of handouts to an all-time high.

The curious public stopped along the streets to pet, take photos, feed and tease the helpless wild animal. As the small male jumped from shoulder to shoulder, attempting to escape the constant harassment, Mickey held tightly to his rein. Before long, the fur wore off the squirrel's wrists, and the skin became raw and sore.

In pain, the squirrel grew mean and threatening, attempting to bite any hand outstretched in his direction. Mickey, having no knowledge of animal behavior, took the inane advice of a friend and determined to neuter the angry squirrel, hoping to halt this aggressive behavior. The unfortunate squirrel survived the surgery, healed, and continued to cling to Mickey's shoulder as they traveled the streets of the city day after day.

Instead of maturing into the sleek, lean wild creature he was meant to be, the young animal grew fat and unhealthy from the steady diet of junk food handed to him by an uninformed public. He continued to display his hatred and mistrust of humans by lashing out at everyone except his master, who was the only world that he knew.

While Mickey and his captive whiled away time in a bar one afternoon, a young man stopped by out of the teeming rain. As the young man sat alone, observing them from a distance, Mickey approached him to ask for a donation. The man contributed the requested money, then turned the conversation toward the squirrel. He asked Mickey how he had acquired the squirrel and learned of the general area they traveled in their daily rounds. Mickey grinned and shrugged when the man mentioned the law against confining wildlife. A few minutes later, the young observer stepped outside the bar, walked to the nearest phone booth and called the Department of Fish and Game. He described in detail the plight and location of the illegally held squirrel.

The Department had no difficulty in locating the well-known panhandler with a squirrel on his shoulder. They transferred the confiscated squirrel to a wildlife center where it promptly bit several volunteers as they tried to dress its wounds and provide it with proper nourishment. When the liability became more than the center could assume, the animal director contacted the Department requesting them to remove the wayward squirrel as soon as a new location could be found.

Captain Rick Harris put in a call to Fawn Rescue seeking help in housing the angry squirrel. I listened with interest and dismay as Captain Harris reviewed the entire squirrel story to date. I learned that this unhappy creature, now one year old, was not a native Western Gray squirrel, but that it had not, as yet, been properly identified. The captain cautioned me about its aggressive behavior and its unhealthy physical condition. Would I, under the circumstances, be willing to assume responsibility for it, he asked. He explained that Mickey had decided to sue the Department for the return of his possession, and, unbelievably, had convinced attorney Broderick Harmon to accept the case. The squirrel must be secured as evidence until after the trial, the captain reminded me, therefore, the confinement might be a lengthy one. Although I knew that the young animal must be healed in both body and mind, learn to recognize his natural foods, and adjust to a wild habitat, I willingly agreed to accept responsibility for his care.

The following morning Mel from Hell, his new name describing his past existence well, arrived at Fawn Rescue, unhealthy and hating the world. His outdoor home in the woods contained tree branches for swinging, climbing and body building. The ground was covered with forest mulch in which to bury food. There were growing plants, wild mushrooms, piles of acorns, pine cones, and all things natural and wild. He found twigs and grasses to store in his nest box, and a deep container of water where he could grip the edge, lean into it and drink in a natural way.

His first few minutes after being placed in the cage were filled with delighted squirrel chatter as he flew from branch to branch, nibbled the bark from tree limbs, and pushed his face deep, deep into the fragrant earth.

Each day, as I approached to refresh his water and renew his supply of fresh foods, he flung himself defiantly against the sides of his cage. He shrieked shrilly at me in rage. I quietly pushed his food through a small opening in the side of the cage and made no attempt to touch or talk to him. Daily, Mel became more accustomed to my silent presence and to the activity of squirrels and other wild creatures surrounding his home in the woods. Visibly he calmed. He jumped, swung and played in greeting. He smelled my hand through the cage and showed no further sign of aggression. His wounds healed, his body grew sleek and muscular, and his fur glistened in the sun.

While Mel adapted to his natural environment, I spent time researching his identity. My research proved beyond any doubt that Mel was an Eastern Gray squirrel, displaying steel gray fur washed with tawny rust on the back, head and feet. A distinctive white fringe brushed the edges of his long bushy tail. We could only speculate on Mel's method of transfer from the eastern to the western borders of the country.

I wrote a letter to the Department of Fish and Game stating my intention to raise this squirrel as a wild animal being readied for freedom. Then, hoping to convince the court of the need to protect these wild creatures, I also wrote to them: "Squirrels are wild and dangerous. They do not make good pets. As they become adults they will demand their freedom and are capable of inflicting injuries on their captors. They are never content to live in confinement, and will make any effort necessary to gain their freedom. They are genetically programmed to be wild and do not adjust to being held captive. Squirrels are born to touch the earth, to swing from tree to tree in obvious joy, and to live in close companionship with their own species. We must respect them for their wildness and not be tempted to deny them their freedom." I could not fathom the possibility of any court considering the return of this now happy and healthy creature back to its original owner, a man who had mutilated and exploited it.

Eventually a most welcome message came to me from Captain Harris. The Department of Fish and Game had granted permission for Mel to be set free when he had been made ready for a safe release. The court case had been dropped, but since I lived in a distant county from the court, I learned none of the details. My focus was on preparing Mel for freedom, so I made no attempt to learn more.

I thought out his release carefully. Because Mel had been neutered, he could not mate with our native squirrels, a risk which would have been against all our policies and principles. By now his temperament had calmed so he posed no threat to other wildlife. They, in turn, displayed no hostility toward him, so he wouldn't be endangered by living among them even though he was a smaller squirrel. I decided it was pointless to transport him back to the east coast, and, instead, set him free on private land where he could be observed carefully and would have a gradual and gentle entry into his new and wild existence.

Mel does not venture from his release site, a grove of dense oak and fir that provides a canopy of protection from predators. Here he continues to live unchallenged by other squirrel species and in harmony with his many companions of the wild.

11
Jac

As do most of my adventures, this tale begins with a phone call. "My name is Vic Anders," the old man said. "We have a fawn lying up against our barn under a bush. He's bleeding and looks like he's in read bad shape. How soon can you be here?" I asked his location. "West of Petaluma, down by the county line. We're in dairy farm land."

I wrote down the directions he gave me, commenting that since it was at least an hour's drive from Fawn Rescue, I was worried that the animal might wander off by that time. "Can you get him into the barn, maybe into a stall for me? Approach him with caution, and be careful of those hoofs," I warned, as I always do.

Without delay, I drove the back roads toward Two Rock. Dairy land spreads for thousands of acres along the Marin County border to the south and reaches west to Tomales Bay. The green rolling hills of spring soon turn a lustrous gold during the heat of summer. Cattle, sheep and horses graze in the peaceful countryside. During the early morning and late evening hours it is not unusual to see deer feeding among them.

Mrs. Anders met me at the front gate. She climbed into the truck to sit on the seat beside me. "I was afraid you'd miss the turn. It's a long way between farms out here. The fawn is back in the field behind the barn. My husband has him secured for you. He wasn't about to let him get away," she said as we drove down the long dirt drive.

"I'm grateful..." I broke off my phrase in horror. For there in the center of a small field stood Anders gripping one end of a fifteen foot rope in his hand, with the other end tied around the neck of the small animal. The frightened captive jerked, jumped and flailed in the air, trying desperately to escape. It screamed in agony and rage.

"Oh, no," I yelled. "It will break its neck!" I stopped the truck, grabbed a blanket and covered the distance between us in an instant. Having no time for a gentle approach, I threw the blanket and my body over the animal and brought it to the ground. As I straddled the violently protesting creature, I wrapped the blanket around its body tightly, then reached under to remove the rope from its neck. I tossed the rope into the dirt and wiped my blood-covered hands on my jeans. As I staggered to my feet, it took all the strength I had to hold this small, but amazingly powerful animal.

Meanwhile the old man had raced up the hill to open the tailgate on my truck.

"What can I do to help?" asked Mrs. Anders.

"It will take two of us to carry this struggling fawn up to the truck. Are you strong enough?"

"I'm a farmer's wife. I'm plenty strong," the frail looking woman commented bluntly. "You're no bigger than a minute yourself."

The two of us had difficulty making it to the truck amid the screams and kicks of the protesting captive.

I placed it in the back of the truck and removed the blanket to check its injuries. "This is no fawn, Mr. Anders," I said in amazement, as I stared at the strange looking male creature standing solidly before me. Blood flowed freely from his mouth and onto the carpeted floor of the camper.

"What is it then?" Mr. Anders asked.

"What is it?" Mrs. Anders echoed.

"I have no idea," I replied. "But when I find out, I'll let you know. Whatever he is, he's in serious trouble and needs immediate attention. I'll get him to my vet at once and call you tonight."

I closed the camper door and took one last look at the odd-looking animal gazing at me in obvious pain. Blood gushed from his split lips and from his bruised, battered nose. His teeth, loose and damaged, slanted to the right of his badly shattered front jaw. His face looked smashed in, as though he had run full force into a solid structure.

On the drive to Dr. Patton's clinic I speculated. Only his face is damaged. His body looks uninjured. If he had been hit head on by a car, he would have been run over and killed. Perhaps he was trying to escape from an enclosure and didn't clear the obstacle. What kind of animal can he be? Where can he have come from? How did he get out here in dairy country? He's neither a domestic animal nor native wildlife — definitely an exotic. I wondered which far away country he came from? Maybe our intriguing friend with the strange antlers is some kind of Pygmy Antelope?

The husky looking animal weighed about twenty pounds and appeared to be full grown. He looked heavier and more stocky than a fawn, with short, narrow legs and tiny, fragile hoofs. The tawny, rust-brown hair covering his body gleamed against his buff colored chest and small white tail. Perhaps his most striking feature was the strange set of antlers, still in velvet. Beginning along either side of his nose, they grew straight up between his eyes, then lay back close to his small erect ears.

Once we arrived at the clinic, Dr. Patton took one quick look and rushed the injured animal directly into X-ray and surgery, with no time wasted on details or explanations.

While I waited for the results of the surgery, I notified the California Department of Fish and Game that I had an exotic in my possession, since my permit covers only native mammals. The Department granted me permission to treat, care for and relocate the animal, giving me complete charge and total responsibility. I would report its identity to them and keep them posted as to its progress and final destination.

The X-rays revealed two fractures to the back of the right jaw which would heal with time. During the extensive surgery, Dr. Patton removed the badly shattered lower jaw and the loosened front teeth. He repaired the upper lip, then folded under and sutured the torn lower lip. He assured me our little invalid would do fine since he would never have to fend for himself as a wild animal. Once he had found a good home with a family to care for him, he could be expected to live a long and happy life. Dr. Patton also explained he would never regain the use of his front jaw, but since his back molars were intact, the injury wouldn't hinder him from chewing and digesting his food.

By the time I had thanked the doctor for coming to my aid once again and set up an appointment to have the stitches removed, our little animal friend had recovered enough to be transferred to Fawn Rescue. He seemed better already. He stood on his feet steady and sure, ready for his second ride in the Fawnmobile. I drove slowly over the country roads thinking that I would first make the recovering animal comfortable in his new home, then do a little research. It will be interesting, I thought, to find out just what kind of creature we had rescued and put back together.

Our newcomer proved to be friendly and tame. He accepted each piece of chopped fruit and each bite of grain I put in his mouth. He nudged toward the alfalfa and fruit tree leaves. He relished it all. He ate his fill, satisfied his thirst, then lay on his bed calmly chewing his cud as he rested.

I settled myself on the floor by his side with my Simon and Schuster's Guide to Mammals. Turning to the ungulate (hoofed animal) section I began flipping pages. No, not that, I mused. No, that's nothing like him either. Several pages later I stopped. Wait. These are similar. I'm getting close. There. Yes, that's him. A Muntjac. He's a Muntiacus Muntjac, an Indian Muntjac, or barking deer. So he is a deer. The description and photo matched perfectly, confirming his identity. I read that a mature Muntjac reaches eighteen to twenty-six inches in height, and thirty-one to thirty-five pounds in weight. Dr. Patton estimated our little male to be close to two years of age. Since he had been neutered, his antlers wouldn't change as he became older. They would never reach maximum growth, nor form the small curved spikes I was looking at in the photo. I continued to read. Twenty subspecies of muntjac are distributed throughout

India, into Indonesia to Java, and through China to Taiwan. Its habitat covers tropical forests to an altitude of ten thousand feet. The muntjac is a solitary and nocturnal herbivore, feeding on fruits, leaves and grasses. It mates year round and gives birth to one or two young. When disturbed, it emits a distinctive noise like a baying dog. A sound I will never forget, I thought, as I closed the book with satisfaction and left the weary muntjac to his rest.

I soon shortened his name to Jac. Jac ate from my hand until he healed well enough to scoop up the food with his turned under lip. He became adept at compensating for the jaw injury. Once his stitches were removed, I transferred him outside. He claimed a vacant fawn enclosure as his own. Daily, this lovable, affectionate creature ran to greet me at the gate and butted against my leg for attention.

At the end of his last examination Dr. Patton pointed to a small tattoo on Jac's ear. I contacted Animal Control, the Humane Society, and local vets. I searched the newspapers daily for any report of a lost muntjac. I found nothing. Had he been held illegally? Had he belonged to a traveling animal show or a petting zoo that had moved on? We were never to know.

During my calls I located a wildlife preserve where exotics were bred for profit. The owner had not lost a muntjac but displayed an interest in this one. I learned they were worth several thousand dollars. The man's interest soon waned as I described the severe injuries and extensive surgery Jac had undergone. "I would suggest you get rid of him," the man said harshly. "He's not worth the money you will have to put into his care."

"You are suggesting that I have him destroyed?" I asked incredulously.

"Why not? He's worthless."

"Worthless in a monetary way, or worthless as a living creature?"

"I have a business to run. I don't have time for any more talk." He hung up the phone abruptly.

Jac needed companionship that I hadn't time to provide. He needed space to wander that I didn't have. The daily demands and responsibilities of Fawn Rescue filled my life. This was my commitment. Jac needed a home, more than just a place to live. He needed a family that would give him the love and attention he deserved. Offers came to me steadily. None of them would do. He would stay with me, and be welcome, until I found the home where I felt he belonged.

One of my friends suggested that Dr. Patton's vet technician Marion James had a perfect home for Jac. Even though I had never been to her home in all the years I'd known her, I knew she would be ideal. I called her at once. She and her family welcomed Jac to join their growing family of farm animals. Their five acres of land on the outskirts of Sebastopol proved to be perfect for this tiny exotic deer. His new home would be a large fenced and secluded piece of land containing shelters, fields, trees and browsing brush. I notified the Department of Fish and Game of the transfer and gave Marian and her husband Rob a letter of permission to have the exotic muntjac in their possession.

Within days Jac and I joined Marian beside one of the stalls in the back of their property. Together we lifted him down out of the truck and placed him in his temporary quarters. Here he would gradually adjust to his new surroundings. He ran the perimeter of the fence, exploring his enclosure. We filled the feed trays with grain, alfalfa and fresh fruit tree leaves. He joined us to drink from the water container, grab a taste of leaves, then resumed his investigation. He gazed through the fence at his future companions, a miniature pony and pygmy goats. I left when he settled to rest on the hay in his shelter.

A few days later Rob and Marian opened the gate to the field. Since the goats were closer to his size and species he accepted them readily enough, but he shied away from the miniature pony that towered over him. Eventually he learned to accept the pony, too, and to enjoy the freedom of the farm. His most firm attachment, however, continues to be the one he has formed with the two boys. He eagerly awaits their visits and runs to the gate to greet them as they call his name. He demands the attention and love they give so gladly. Jac has become an important part of their lives.

12

Can't Buy the World

The permit issued to wildlife organizations by the California Department of Fish and Game states that each facility is responsible for its own funding. These centers approach this challenge in many creative ways. Some have large membership drives. Some request grants from charitable foundations. Small centers hold the usual dinners, bazaars, raffles and car washes.

Each spring, before the arrival of fawns, Fawn Rescue held a yearly flea market as its major fund raising event. The profits we deposited into our account had to last for the rest of the year. Once fawn season began, no time could be spared, no energy wasted, for any purpose but the care of the young animals.

During the year I collected items to clean and sort, label and price, pack and store. I drove across town to be handed a bag of used clothing, damaged household goods and useless magazines. Other times I picked up valuable resale items, such as a truckload of worthwhile left overs donated from an entire estate sale. Friends faithfully collected donations and delivered them to Fawn Rescue.

Weekly I sorted, discarded, and cleaned the items as they arrived. I boxed and stored them for the big day. The recycling center donated their twenty-foot truck to transport my yearly collection to the site of the huge sale. I rented space at a public flea market that covered acres of land and attracted carloads of buyers searching for bargains. Tables filled with merchandise sold for very low prices. Yet in spite of the tremendous effort put into this project, the benefits were often too small to provide for our needs. As the organization grew, so did the flea market. It became an overwhelming and exhausting job even with the help of many friends. I began to search for a better way to provide for my ever increasing budget.

Late one afternoon a woman named Amy Jarvis called with an offer to help. "We've met at various wildlife meetings," she began. "You remember — I work for Mr. Earl Cartwright. I've mentioned Fawn Rescue to him many times."

"Yes, I remember you, Amy. Are you having a problem I can help you with?"

"Well, that's a good way to put it. Yes, it is a problem that you can help with. But the best part of it is that Mr. Cartwright can help you in a very big way in return." I wasn't sure what she was getting at. "I told him how hard you work getting those flea markets organized every year. How much do you make at one?"

"Just barely enough to scrape by until the next one," I answered. "I am looking for other options, however. Do you have an idea?"

"More than an idea. This is a real proposition. You'll never have to hold another fund raiser again. How does that sound?"

"Unbelievable. Has Mr. Cartwright decided to sponsor Fawn Rescue as a tax write off?." I had heard that this man was a millionaire, but his role as a philanthropist was never mentioned. I had never met him and couldn't understand his sudden interest in my small organization about which he knew nothing.

"Not an outright sponsorship, but let me explain. Mr. Cartwright owns thousands of acres of prime forest land along one of the major rivers in Northern California. He enjoys spending time up there. He's quite interested in wildlife. He mentioned there are still a few bear and elk on his land, but the supply of game, especially deer, is becoming short."

"Amy, when you used the word 'game," my stomach just turned over. You know how I feel about killing wildlife simply for sport."

"Listen, Maggie, let me explain our idea. I'm a hunter myself," she began.

"But you belong to a wildlife group, don't you?"

"Yes, but they're separate. I enjoy them both. One has nothing to do with the other."

"I can't understand the separation, but tell me why you called." I felt myself tensing, filled with suspicion.

"Well, Mr. Cartwright is an avid hunter, as you must know. He's famous for his skills. He trophy hunts all over the world. It's something he enjoys, Maggie. You shouldn't hold it against him. He's a kind and generous man, as you'll soon realize."

"Yes, I'm aware of your boss's hunting safaris, and I don't judge him for it. His hobby has nothing to do with me. I don't answer for him. He makes his choices, as we all do." I stopped, realizing that perhaps I did sound judgmental after all. Then I continued, "I'm not sure where this conversation is leading."

"I just want to make sure you understand where we're coming from with our proposal. We don't want you to have any wrong ideas about our motives. Believe me when I say we want to help you financially. You work too hard, and Mr. Cartwright can make things easier for you."

"Okay, go on." I became more apprehensive as the conversation continued.

"Mr. Cartwright said to tell you he'll fly you up to his wilderness area so you can see for yourself what prime deer territory it is."

"Oh, are you offering me a release site? Humbolt County's too far. I release all of them in Sonoma County, which is where they are born."

"Yes, a release site. But even better, he'll donate one hundred dollars for each fawn you release on his land. Isn't that fantastic? How many fawns have you had so far this year?" she asked.

"Fifty two." I said, my voice still and controlled.

"Fifty two!" she gushed. "Just think, that's five thousand, two hundred dollars for your organization. No more fund raisers for you. Isn't that great?"

I felt stunned, outraged. I found it difficult to speak. The insult twisted sharply into my senses. I took a deep breath before replying, "Mr. Cartwright realizes, of course, that these are not all bucks that I release. I'm assuming that he wants these fawns to hunt for pleasure. Does he hunt females, too?"

"Oh, certainly he knows they're not all bucks. But the does have babies, so that's okay. One hundred dollars no matter what the sex. He'll take whatever you provide," she offered.

Not believing the direction this conversation was taking, I answered, "Mr. Cartwright must surely know that buying and selling wildlife is illegal."

"It won't be considered buying and selling. We can get around that well enough. He'll be providing a release site for your fawns, and because he's interested in your project, he'll become Fawn Rescue's sponsor. How's that?" Amy replied enthusiastically. She seemed certain that I would be convinced and would consider Fawn Rescue's financial needs realistically.

"So, this property is being used as a hunting camp and nothing more?"

"Well, yes, but understand, he and his friends don't just shoot everything that moves."

"Then why has the deer herd become nonexistent? Why does he need to replenish the land every year with my fawns? Why is he willing to pay thousands of dollars each year for new blood?" My voice rose in fury.

"Wait, Maggie..."

"No, you wait. First of all, I am having a hard time believing I heard you right, or that you would even consider calling me with such an insane proposition. You've known me for years. This is a tremendous insult. What do you think Fawn Rescue is all about? Why do you think I do this? Why would I need money to raise potentially dead fawns? Why not let them die in the first place?" I raged. "I have vets who donate their time, skills, and money to help me keep these fawns alive. Do you think I could betray their trust or the trust of the people who bring these fawns to me for care? Do you think I get up at 3 a.m. to drive fifty miles for a fawn so that Mr. Cartwright can use it as a target? Not my fawns," I concluded, "You tell Mr. Cartwright, for me, that he can't buy the world."

"Think about it, Maggie, and call me back," she said cheerfully. "I think you'll see things differently when you calm down." It seemed that she hadn't heard a word I said. I knew the message never got through to her.

Although our paths crossed at wildlife meetings, Amy never put the proposition before me again.

*

I recall the friendliness in the man's voice when I answered the phone one late afternoon. "My name's Harry Langly. Are you the lady I just saw on the TV program about Fawn Rescue?"

"Are they still showing that on Channel 50?" I asked. "They made an interesting story of our project here, didn't they? I'm glad to hear the word is still getting out about what we do."

"It was interesting. I never knew there was a place that specialized in fawns. And right here in Sonoma County, at that. While I was watching, I had an idea that maybe you can help me with."

"I'll do whatever I can, Mr. Langly. Tell me your idea."

"I've known my friend Marty for more years than I like to think about," he began. "We were buddies when we both lived in Southern California. Since I moved up here we don't see each other so often. He's become wealthy over the years. I never managed to do that. He's always doing things for me, and I can never find anything I can give him in return that he doesn't already have. He's impossible to buy for. I'd like to give him a gift he'd never forget, and one he wouldn't buy for himself."

"That's thoughtful of you." I assumed he might want to bring his friend on a tour of the facility, or have a photo taken with a fawn. These requests are not unusual. Artists, photographers, teachers and other professionals offer a few dollars to use the fawns as props in their work. If I accepted their offers and exploited the fawns for profit, I would no longer have to be concerned with finances. I've found ways of refusing people without offending them. I remind them that my permit forbids Fawn Rescue to be open to the public. I explain that fawns must retain their natural fear of humans in order for them to remain wild. Most people understand without further question.

"Here's the situation," he continued. "Marty owns a large piece of land in Beverly Hills. It's completely fenced. He has beautiful gardens and landscaping. Gigantic white gardenia bushes, spectacular fuchsia, multi-colored hibiscus, brilliant bougainvillea, all the gorgeous tropical plants we can't grow up here. He has pecan, avocado and citrus trees laden with fruit. There's a spectacular three-point buck that leaps over that high fence like it wasn't even there. The most beautiful thing you ever saw. Marty loves watching that buck. He doesn't care what he eats or destroys. He has a gardener who takes care of all that. They put out fruit to encourage the buck to come in."

"I've seen bucks hurdle a fence." I answered. "Pure grace in motion — a rare treat, especially in Beverly Hills. That reminds me of a ballet I saw in Mexico City," I continued. "One of the dancers portrayed a stag. The power and elegance of his movements were spectacular, and yet, it's only an imitation, isn't it?"

"I'll get to the point," he said. "I got to thinking when I saw your fawns on TV what a fantastic gift two of those little females would make for my friend. It would be a gift no one would ever top. He could put them in the fenced yard where they'd be company for each other. They'd be cared for and protected. Best of all, the buck would be enticed to visit more often," he finished triumphantly. His manner told me that he meant no harm. He just didn't understand wildlife.

"Mr. Langly, did you ever stop to think that the buck would lead those does out over the fence as soon as they grew a little older?" I laughed.

"I don't think so. They'd be at home. Why would they want to leave?"

"Because they're wild. They would never stay. They might visit now and then to help the buck devour the garden, but they'd be out over the fence with him when they'd had enough. Besides, it's against the law to hold wildlife captive," I told him.

"They wouldn't be captive. They'd have the whole run of his estate. Plenty of room for them to roam and plenty of food to eat."

"That sounds logical, I know," I agreed. "But I can't sell my fawns. That, too, is against the law. These are wild creatures. They don't want to be pets. They become dangerous as they mature. It would be a real liability for your friend, even if it were legal. Sorry to have to turn you down. I can see that they would make an unusual gift, but I just can't do it."

"We're talking big bucks, if you'll excuse the pun," he laughed, reluctant to give up. "I'd be willing to give you top dollar for two of those little does."

"Believe me, there's no way it can happen. It has nothing to do with money. It has to do with the law that protects wildlife, and their instinctive need for freedom. There are some things that money can't buy, Mr. Langly, and wildlife is one of them. Sorry," I finished, hoping for his understanding.

"Well, okay. I guess it wasn't such a good idea, after all."

"Just wait, some other great gift will come along for you to give Marty. I know it." I smiled as I placed the receiver in its cradle.

13

A Cry in the Dark

One dreary, dismal morning in early spring, I answered the phone to hear Cora Clark relate a story I still recall with horror. She began by telling me that just before dark the night before, she and her husband heard an ungodly screaming and thrashing in their back woods. They ran out to find a doe twisting on the ground in agony. The doe had just given birth to a fawn and seemed to be having trouble delivering the sibling. Mrs. Clark went on to explain in a thin, vapid voice, "As we approached the writhing mother, the newborn fawn jumped away from her side and managed to conceal itself in the brush. Because of the pouring rain and the cold, we didn't try to pursue the fawn. We decided to leave and let nature work it out."

"What happened? Are they all right now?" I asked anxiously.

"It rained and stormed all night—horrible weather," she droned on, as I impatiently wondered when she would tell me why she had called for my help. "We never heard another sound from the doe after we walked away. We found her still lying there this morning in the same spot. She died before giving birth to the second fawn."

"I wish you had called me then. I could have at least tried to help her. I'm sorry she died so horribly. But you do have the first-born fawn for me now, Mrs. Clark?"

"Well, no. That's why I'm calling you," she answered. "We could hear it crying weakly out there all night, but it was raining too hard to even think of looking for it in the dark. We went out this morning, and all of a sudden, it's not crying anymore. Why would it just stop crying? We can't see it now and don't have time to look for it. We're leaving for work. Can you come over and look around? We won't be here, but you have our permission to search all you want."

Trying hard to control my feeling of aversion and allowing none of it to creep into my voice, I asked for precise directions to the property, knowing the Clarks wouldn't be available again. I placed the phone receiver in its cradle, picked up my wallet, and ran out the door. While driving through the canyon, I reviewed the circumstances as I understood them. I realized how remote the chance would be to find a quiet, hiding newborn fawn, if it still lived. This fawn had never nursed, and it had no protection from the rain and cold. The stress of crying all night, alone and hungry, would be enough to kill it.

The house number clearly showed on an old mailbox along the side of the canyon road. A dirt drive led through pastures and past barns containing several horses. The house nestled among a grove of trees. I parked in front, pulled on my rain jacket, and made my way toward the back. I climbed a small grade and turned to walk into the tall wet weeds and dripping trees where Mrs. Clark had said the doe would be. I found her at once. She lay twisted and dead in the drizzling rain. The grass lay leveled around her where she had struggled. A deep sadness swept over me as I stooped to touch her still, cold body. I could see the tip of the hoofs of her unborn fawn. I wondered, as I gazed at her with sorrow, if I could have saved this doe and her fawn had I been called last night while she still lived. Why did they wait until morning to call? How could they sleep while an orphaned fawn cried in distress in the pouring rain? They had seen the fawn on its feet, alert enough to hide and strong enough to cry for help. It surely could have been rescued. How could they not have made the attempt?

I searched for an hour. I pleaded silently for the fawn to show itself as I crawled through the woods. To call aloud would cause it to shrink deeper into its hiding place. My efforts seemed futile in this large brush-covered area. Time was running out. The fawn must be dead by now, I thought, but I can't stop looking until I know for certain. It could be anywhere, so small and camouflaged. I needed help. I rushed home to bring my husband back to help with the search. We combed every inch of the woods, branching out from the spot where the doe lay. The fawn could not, and would not, have moved far from her body. Why couldn't we find it? In frustration we crawled through the wet weeds and grasses. We pushed aside each branch of dripping brush. We continued searching for another hour. We couldn't leave until we knew the fate of this newborn creature.

Finally, my husband called in a hushed voice, "Here it is." He walked toward me with a sopping wet four-pound fawn in his arms. As he stood beside me, she opened her eyes, looked up and gave a tiny thin cry, then weakly closed her eyes again.

"Oh, she's alive!" I cried. We rushed toward the truck, grabbed clean dry towels, and as my husband wiped, dried and warmed her icy body against his chest, I drove frantically down the curving grade and through the ten miles of hills toward the vet clinic, knowing that Dr. Patton would be just opening for the day. "He'll know what to do for this baby," I said, full of optimism.

We pulled into the parking lot and dashed through the front door of the clinic. The receptionist immediately ushered us back into the emergency room where Dr. Patton stood viewing an X-ray. He looked up in surprise to ask, "What is it, Maggie? What's wrong?" I unwrapped the fawn, but too late. Her tiny cold body lay still in the towel. Her plaintive cry in the woods had been her last. Her small life gone too soon.

I grieved as we drove home. "She could have lived. She could have lived. Why didn't they call me last night? How could anyone lie in the comfort of a warm bed, listening to the cry of a helpless fawn, alone in the rain and darkness, and not respond? What kind of a barbaric world do we live in?"

14

A Risky Rescue

This case began like so many others. The caller wanted only information. The woman sounded stressed, saying that she had only a minute because she had a plane to catch. "I almost forgot to call you before I left," said Mrs. Barry Hart. "We have a darling fawn here at my vineyard and I promised to find out what to feed it. It seems very ill with diarrhea."

Since she showed no inclination to give the fawn to me, I knew I must talk fast or my chance to find it would be gone. "Where are you located, Mrs. Hart? Where did you get the fawn, and how long have you had it? What are you feeding it?" The questions poured out.

"The vineyard worker's children found it in our field several days ago. I'd guess they're giving it cow's milk. I'm not sure. They kept it for the children to play with after school. I can't see any reason to take it away from them."

"Where did you say you live?"

"We own a vineyard up on Vineyard Road in Healdsburg. But why the questions? I'm pressed for time. Tell me what they should feed it." Her voice rose in agitation.

"Mrs. Hart, please listen. This won't take long. First, are you aware that it's against the law to keep wildlife as a pet? Also, consider the liability if the fawn injures one of the children," I warned. "The fawn should never have been picked up. The mother was close by foraging for food. The cow's milk they're feeding it hasn't the richness to sustain a fawn. That's why it has diarrhea, which will lead to dehydration and death. Please let me come for it right away. Time is crucial to its survival."

"That's not necessary. I'll buy the formula from you. I don't want to cause trouble with my workers. They come back to work on my ranch every year, and I can't afford to lose them over a deer."

"Believe me, the fawn is dying. The stress, combined with the illness, will kill it within a few days. An animal that young has no reserves. Please let me pick it up. If not, I'll report it to the Department of Fish and Game, and you'll be forced to relinquish it anyway, plus pay a substantial fine."

"Well, I'm on my way out of town. I'll be gone for several weeks. If you come for it, I don't want to be responsible either way," she responded.

"Then I have permission to come on your land?"

"Do what you like. I don't have any more time to discuss this with you." She hung up abruptly.

I left for Healdsburg immediately. Though I had no address, I did have a name and general location. How many vineyards could there be on Vineyard Road? The name should have given me a clue. I passed miles and miles of vineyards in my search. I stopped at a fork in the road, not knowing which direction to take. As if by providence, my eye caught the name Barry Hart clearly marked on one of a group of mailboxes mounted on posts along the road. To the right then. That gravel road must lead to the Harts' vineyard, I thought. It proved not to be that easy. On my route I wound through hills, then turned into an archway leading to a luxurious, top-of-the-hill home. Several people sat on a shaded deck enjoying the view and a drink. I offered my brochure and explained my mission.

"We're new to the area. Sorry we don't know where you might find the Hart residence. This is not the place," a woman informed me.

I drove into each driveway, into canyons, and through more miles of vineyards. Occasionally I saw groups of field workers off in the distance who waved as I drove by. I checked and eliminated five vineyard markers along dusty, endless dirt roads. Finally, as I rounded a bend, a truck came toward me over the horizon. I parked my pickup at the bottom of the steep grade, jumped out, and stepped into the middle of the road. The driver pulled to a halt and leaned his head out the window inquiringly.

"Do you know of a ranch where they're keeping a fawn?" I asked. He shrugged and answered in Spanish. He spoke only Spanish, and I spoke only English. I made ridiculous motions, putting on quite a performance to the astonishment of the driver. I tried o describe a baby deer. I made long ears on my head. I made leaping motions with my arms. Then I began to laugh. My actions could have described a hare, as well as a fawn. The driver smiled politely and shook his head. I motioned for him to wait. Why didn't I think of this before? I ran back to the truck to grab a brochure. I pointed to the fawn on the cover. The man broke into an eager smile. "Si," he said, and motioned for me to follow.

A mile along the curving road we turned into a well-maintained complex of horse barns, training stables, and an enormous maintenance barn. We stopped outside the back entrance to a building containing tractors and other large ranch equipment. I grabbed a blanket from behind the seat, jumped out of the Fawnmobile, and slammed the door behind me. The deafening din of the equipment vibrated through the barn as we moved inside.

The young ranch worker reached down to pull a small airline carrier out from against the wall and placed it by my feet. He stooped down to point to the male fawn no more than a few days old. Blood oozed from wounds on his head where he had beat it against the bars trying to escape his prison. A loose, watery stool streamed down his legs, forming pools on the carrier floor. There was no turning room in the cage. He must either stand facing forward, or lie in the contamination. I opened the door to lift the fawn out and hold him close. Trembling in terror, he fought for freedom. When I stood up with the fawn still in my arms, my guide became apprehensive. He motioned in a manner that said, "Is this your fawn?" I nodded my head "yes" and went into my act again. I showed him that the fawn was ill, and I would care for him until he got well. I made sweeping motions with my arms to say that I would set the fawn free.

The man nervously indicated that I should return the fawn to his cage. Once again, he said, "Is this your fawn?" This time I said, "Si," and gave him the brochure I still had clutched in my hand. On it I wrote my name and pointed to myself. I told him to tell his manager that it was this person who took the fawn. The young man seemed to understand and was comfortable with that solution. I mentioned Mrs. Hart's name and pointed to the fawn. He smiled and repeated Mrs. Hart's name, "Si, Mrs. Hart," and waved his hand toward the west of the property. Satisfied, the man stepped to one side to allow me to pass with the fawn in my arms.

I hurried to the truck and reached for the door. It was locked. My purse with the extra set of keys lay inside on the floor. I frantically tugged at the door. I scanned the tightly shut windows. The young man saw my panic and shrugged his shoulders in sympathy.

There was nothing he could do to help. As a gesture, he peered under the hood, then shook his head.

Just then, down the drive from the horse barns, came a hefty, red-faced woman behind the wheel of an electric cart. Her sweat-stained shirt clung to her muscular body. She pulled her fingers through thick blond hair, then wiped them on her dusty jeans and stared at me coldly. "What's going on down here? Who are you, and what do you want?" She stepped out of the cart to tower over me.

I identified myself, informing her that Mrs. Hart gave me permission to pick up this fawn. "It's near death. I'm taking it with me for care."

"Mrs. Hart? Are you sure?" she asked suspiciously.

"Of course. How else would I have known it was here? How would I have found it?" I asked, never glancing in the direction of the worried young man standing beside me.

"I don't like the whole idea.." she began. I interrupted to ask her name. "Olga. I'm the manager."

"Well, Olga, I have a problem. I've locked myself out of my truck, and I'm going to have to use your phone. Is there one in the horse barn?" I looked her boldly in the eye, never allowing her to guess how nervous I was.

"Get in the cart, and I'll drive you up. We have a phone in my office you can use," she mumbled. I climbed in beside her, holding the fawn tightly against me, keeping him out of view. No need to remind her of my mission.

I dialed information and then Triple A. I explained to dispatch that I was on an animal emergency rescue and needed quick response. The Road Service driver called me at once for directions. "You'll have a difficult time finding me," I fretted. "I don't even know where I am."

"Do you have an address? I've been in every canyon in Healdsburg. I'll find you," she assured me. I asked Olga for the address and repeated her reply to the driver. "See you in a half hour," she promised. "I'm not that far from there."

"Hurry," I pleaded. I walked to the top of the hill and sat on a rock where I had a good view of any arriving vehicles. The fawn lay limp and still in my arms. I held him gently, without talking, anxious to get him back to Fawn Rescue for care. I stood up to wave as the service truck pulled into view. When the driver stopped, I climbed in and directed her past the horse barns and on to the maintenance section of the ranch where my Fawnmobile sat tightly locked and waiting.

"Oh, a little pickup. No problem," she said cheerfully. She pulled out a small thin tool and expertly maneuvered it down through the side of the door. The lock clicked open. "Simple," she laughed.

"For you," I said with relief. I carefully placed the fawn in the back and followed the service truck through the maze of roads to the highway where I was once again in familiar territory.

On the long drive home my mind wandered back to the many times each spring that I have rescued fawns taken from their mothers. There is no comparable substitute for nature, I thought. For these self-appointed care givers, once the fun of bottle feeding the baby is over, they lose interest. If the fawn lives, as it grows older it becomes unruly and unwanted by its captors, who then set it free in the wrong habitat and without the proper skills to survive. Often it dies of stress even before it starves. At Fawn Rescue, I do what I can to prepare these animals for their lives in the wild. I teach them to recognize their natural foods and to retain their instinctive fear of man, but I can never replace a mother's care and training.

I attended to the ill fawn at home. He permitted me to clean and dress the abrasions on his head. He finished the bottle I offered, then lay curled in his bed, exhausted from his ordeal. I felt encouraged that he responded so well. He'll be fine, I thought. The will to live reflected strongly from his soft brown eyes. I left him to rest for the night and went to mix bottles for the other hungry fawns. As they drank, I heard the shrill ring of the phone. I raced up the stairs from the pen to answer. Why does it wait until I'm down here to ring, I thought irritably. "Fawn Rescue," I said. "This is Maggie."

"I know who you are," said the angry, threatening voice. "I got your name from this brochure you left with one of our workers. It also has your address. This is Olga."

"Yes..."

"The ranch kids came home from school to find their fawn gone. Now they're yelling and crying. I'm responsible for keeping these workers happy around this vineyard. We can't afford to have them take off at this time of year. They're needed until after the harvest. I'm calling to tell you that if you don't have that fawn back here before dark, we're coming after it."

"Olga, please listen. The fawn is nearly dead. He would have died overnight in your barn. The children wouldn't have it anyway. Do you want them to have that kind of experience? Do you want the fawn to die?"

"I don't care if the fawn does die. There are hundreds of them out there in the woods. This fawn is theirs. Something new. Every night they have fun pulling him out of his crate and giving him the bottle. When they get through playing, they put him back in the barn."

"No wonder he's dying," I replied angrily. "Olga, has anyone told you it's against the law to hold wildlife captive? With good reason. What kind of lesson does that teach the children? That it's okay to disobey the law and to mistreat animals? Besides, there's a large fine if you're caught with any captive wildlife, not just fawns."

"So what? We'll pay the fine. We can afford it, if it's money you want. It's our fawn, anyway."

"No. That's not the way it works. You can't buy wildlife. If I hadn't personally come after it, it would have been confiscated by the Department of Fish and Game, and then you would have been issued a citation."

"I didn't call to argue law." Olga's voice and words were becoming heavy and slurred. She cursed through every sentence. I realized I couldn't reason with her if she had been drinking.

"Will you allow me to come up to talk to the children?" I suggested hopefully. "I don't like the idea of them thinking the deer was taken from them for no reason. I can explain to them the difference between wildlife and domestic animals. I can make them understand. It would be such a good lesson for them, and this could be changed from a bad experience to one they could accept."

"The only visit that's going to be made is when we come down there and tear that place apart," she screamed. Her language became more abusive with every word.

Finally, I had enough. "Don't try to intimidate me, Olga." My voice was cold with anger. "I'm not the least afraid of your threats. I can promise you that you'll not see this fawn again. If you don't take my word for it, perhaps you'd enjoy a visit from the Department of Fish and Game. I'll call them with my report when I hang up." As more curses poured through the phone, I hung up. I made a formal report to the Department. In spite of my bravado, I worried that my facility might be sabotaged. I slept uneasily that night.

By law, Fawn Rescue is not permitted to be open to the public. For that reason, I have no name, address, or phone number painted on the Fawnmobile. We do not advertise our location. We allow no one, other than authorized personnel, access to the facility. As a result of this incident, I revised Fawn Rescue's literature, such as stationery, brochures, and business cards to reflect our business post office box number rather than our physical address.

Also, as a result of my report, a warden from the Department of Fish and Game phoned the manager of the Hart ranch to explain the law regarding illegal possession of wildlife and to confirm my statement to her that the fawn would remain at Fawn Rescue.

The small buck gradually responded to the medication, the proper diet, and the association with his own species. Months later, fully recovered from his trauma, he joined the others in his group for release on a one-thousand-acre wooded lake site to enjoy a free, natural life far from humanity.

15

The Jogging Bandit

The woman called from a pay phone in Penngrove. "I got your number from Animal Control," she said. "I just saw a fawn get side swiped by a car. It may not be hurt too badly. It's still on its feet, but it was definitely hit. The traffic's heavy there, and I'm afraid it may be hit again. It's standing along Petaluma Road. Do you know where that is?"

"I must know every road in the county by now," I assured her. "Can you give me the crossroad?" She said it was just down from Roberts Road on the right.

The half hour drive through winding Bennett Valley, over the top of Grange Road and down into Crane Canyon is always lovely, whatever the season. Now the spring rain soaked deep into the earth, causing the hills to come alive with a mosaic of brilliant colors. The dark green of the scrub oak glistened wetly. Spires of blue lupine, mingled with the vibrant golds of the California poppy, shone above the shimmering green carpet that spread for miles across the rolling hills.

I parked at the spot the caller had described and walked slowly along both sides of the road looking for the fawn. When an animal is not severely injured, it recovers, moves back into the hills, and is never seen again. This was one of those times. Nevertheless, I decided to retrace my steps to investigate a black plastic bag sitting upright on the shoulder of the road. Fawns that have died before I arrive are sometimes put in a box or covered with newspaper. Thinking this could be my fawn, I touched the bag carefully with my shoe. Traffic zoomed by dangerously close, so I put the bag into the back of the truck and drove to a turnout where I felt safe to examine my find. A quick glance inside revealed not a fawn, but a collection of purses, cosmetic bags, and a carrying case. Well, I thought, I just picked up a nice black bag of rubbish. I'll throw it away when I get home.

Once home, before leaving the garage, I inquisitively dumped the jingling contents of the bag onto the tailgate of the truck. Out tumbled an array of jewelry. The containers were filled with good quality costume jewelry and keepsakes. Necklaces, bracelets, earrings, pins and chains were tangled together in a jumbled mass. Some looked old, but none of great value, except one old string of pearls.

I carried the jewelry into the house to examine it more closely. I glanced through it, but soon lost interest. The assortment hardly looked like one person's collection. It represented a variety of tastes. This large collection spread out on the table before me brought to mind the costume jewelry we had on display at our wildlife flea markets.

Having no interest in the collection, I called a friend who sold antique jewelry at exhibits. I described my find to her, then said, "Ruth, if you want it, you can have it all. Some of it may be old, but I know nothing about jewelry."

"I'd love to have it, Maggie. You never know what might sell. Do you want a percentage of the sales for Fawn Rescue?"

"No, of course not," I answered. "This is a good way to thank you for all the hours you've donated to my fund raisers. I'll drop it off one day this week. See you then."

The night after I delivered the jewelry to her, Ruth called. "Maggie, my daughter and I spent hours going through this jewelry. We stayed up half the night. I found initials on some of it that match the name of a Mrs. Grayson, who's been mentioned in the newspaper recently. I felt I should talk to you before calling the woman," she said nervously. "The article mentioned a robbery."

"A robbery? Really? That stuff just looked like junk to me. Shows how much I know. Sure, Ruth, call the woman and find out more about it."

"My main concern is involving you," she said. "I don't want to make trouble for you, but if I call her, how can I say where it came from without telling her the whole story?"

"By all means tell the whole story, and, of course, use my name. I've nothing to hide, and neither have you. Give her my phone number if you like. I'll back you up, whatever you say." I began to laugh. "She may find the truth hard to believe. You know the old stranger-than-fiction line. Most people don't pick up garbage bags along the road to check for bodies."

Later that day, Ruth called again. "Mrs. Grayson came to the house and identified some of the jewelry and a purse. The robber is no novice. All the valuable jewelry is missing. But most of the items belonging to her, like the pearl necklace, were old family keepsakes that can't be replaced. She's happy to have them returned to her."

"Interesting. I hope this helps identify the thief."

"The Grayson home is not the only one that's been robbed," Ruth added. "The paper refers to him as the jogging bandit. He jogs by remote homes in wealthy neighborhoods to learn the homeowner's habits. He's robbed dozens of homes throughout the county."

I began to comment, but my conscientious friend interrupted me. "I'm not through, yet. Now I feel that it's important to notify the Sheriff's Department. And again, I don't know how you feel about becoming involved."

"Just the way I felt the first time you asked. Give them the entire story, plus my name and phone number. Neither of us have done anything wrong. I'll have to admit I was terribly naive not to have even given robbery a thought," I answered. "You think more logically than I do. You certainly put a lot of very small facts together to make your case. Maybe the Sheriff's Department needs to hire you."

Later that day a deputy from the Sheriff's Department picked up the jewelry. He wasn't pleased that Ruth had permitted Mrs. Grayson to claim some of the items before notifying his office. Ruth justified her action by pointing out that until Mrs. Grayson had identified the jewelry, she didn't know it was stolen property, and would have put it on sale at her next show. She reminded the deputy that she had notified his office as soon as she had all the facts.

The next morning Deputy Loman phoned me to verify Ruth's story. "Run that by me again. We're familiar with what you do, but you'll have to admit this is a strange story."

I admitted that I do seem to become involved in some odd situations now and then. "This is one of the better ones," I answered, as I related my story once more.

From time to time a news article mentions a new robbery by the jogger and a few more pieces of the recovered jewelry are identified by the owners. But the mystery of why a plastic bag full of jewelry was lying by the side of Petaluma Hill Road has never been solved.

16
Caesarean

Del Klamen slammed on his truck brakes as he rounded a sharp curve on Occidental Road, but not in time to avoid the pregnant doe as she bounded down the embankment and directly into the path of his pickup. He pulled to a stop and ran back to the deer lying on the shoulder of the road where she had been thrown by the impact. Filled with remorse, he reached to touch her inert body and noticed a movement within her rounded belly. The fawn still lived. He could feel the shin of its foreleg actively kick and move under his fingers.

Klamen had some knowledge of deer anatomy due to his many years as a hunter, so without hesitation, he pulled a six-inch knife from his pocket and knelt to perform an unprofessional, but successful, roadside Caesarean section on the dead doe. He cut the umbilical cord with this same knife and carefully lifted out the newborn fawn, massaged its ribs and cleaned its mouth. The fawn's heart beat strongly, and it drew a sharp breath as Klamen continued to massage the wet, limp body into life. As darkness closed in, the young man left the doe where she lay, wrapped the tiny male in a towel, and placed it on his lap for the race home.

Unaware that wildlife help is available around the clock, Klamen cleaned the fawn at home, then wrapped it snugly in a blanket. Soon the spunky little buck stood shakily on his feet demanding nourishment. Klamen offered the newborn a bottle of soy formula he borrowed from a neighbor, then later, warm cow's milk, hoping it would suffice until morning when he planned to get it under the care of a wildlife expert. During its first night of life, the fawn slept in a cozy box close beside Klamen's bed.

By morning the small creature had developed diarrhea as a result of the mixture of indigestible food Klamen had given it, the trauma of the unnatural birth, and lack of the essential mother's first milk. Improper diet can kill even healthy wild young ones. This newborn had no reserves to fight so powerful a combination of strikes against his welfare. The definite signs of illness made Klamen anxious to transfer the fawn to Fawn Rescue, although he confessed that he had difficulty in parting with this particular little buck that had so quickly become a part of his life.

Navajo, named for his red-rock-desert coloring, weighed in at just over five pounds, a normal weight for a full-term fawn. I placed him in a warm isolated indoor shelter. Since the fawn had never nursed from his natural mother, it was crucial that I locate a reasonable substitute for the colostrum, a mother's first milk, which normally provides immunities from infection until the baby is able to develop its own immunities. The transfer of these immunities from the doe to fawn is essential for the young one's survival. I contacted a nearby Nubian goat farmer who provided fresh goat colostrum, the only substitute available. As Navajo drank hungrily, I hoped the nourishment, given him during his first twenty-four hours of life, would help him overcome this serious handicap to his health.

The days continued to be rainy and cold. Navajo remained indoors where he could be carefully monitored and fed the goat colostrum during his first two days. The diarrhea slowed as he gained strength. His diet gradually included more and more of the doe milk replacer on which the other fawns flourished.

Navajo's story spread by word of mouth, and soon the news of this unusual event reached the local newspapers. After interviewing Del Klamen, reporters called Fawn Rescue for further details and photos. It is against our policy to expose fawns to outside contact. However, on rare occasions, an exception is made in order to alert the public to the dangers with which wildlife is confronted. This time I considered carefully before granting permission for photos to be taken of this exceptional little buck. When the newspaper crew arrived, I carried him outside to place him gently on the grass for his publicity shots. Quickly, the crew snapped photos of Navajo, and I returned him to his sanctuary at once. Soon the traumatic birth of this fawn became front page news.

This publicity brought our celebrity buck to the attention of television stations. Channel 50 in Santa Rosa closed its evening newscast with a touching few minutes of the remarkable story of the roadside Caesarean birth. Navajo became famous, and within days the story traveled to other parts of the state. Since it is also important for the public to be made aware of the work that is being done to benefit wildlife, I granted one more short interview the following week to a network from San Francisco. They sought permission to incorporate Navajo's story into a ten minute segment of a well-known weekly animal program.

The station invited Klamen to participate. He took time from his job in construction to join the television crew at Fawn Rescue. Lights and cameras were set up on the lawn, and Klamen related once more the tale of the tragic accident and his quick response to it. Our tiny unconcerned star of the show showed more interest in staggering around on his spindly legs, poking his nose into crevices, than he did to the surrounding activity. During the few minutes in which he made his appearance, he hovered close to my side, his surrogate mother and all that he knew.

The camera crew taped the story quickly and efficiently. To make certain of their success with the filming, they replayed a small portion of it on the playback machine mounted in their vehicle. Once satisfied, they packed up their equipment and left. Navajo had long since retired to his bed after his first real outdoor venture. This excellent human-interest film was shown on television several times within the next few weeks, then became a periodic segment of a back roads travel program.

Navajo seemed to gain strength daily. He thrived on the doe formula and ran to the divider to grab his bottle enthusiastically. His attempt to jump over the three-foot fence that kept him confined, displayed an amazing amount of power in those fragile looking legs.

At two weeks of age, just as I considered allowing him to join the older fawns outdoors, he suddenly showed signs of weakening and lack of appetite. He approached the bottle to grab eagerly, suck an ounce, then stop. No amount of coaxing would entice him to drink more of his usual eight ounces. Several trips to Dr. Patton's vet clinic revealed no reason for this sudden change in his habits. He became lethargic, lacking energy and appetite. We gave him medication to combat a sudden fever. We considered the trauma of his mother's death, his unusual birth, the unsanitary conditions under which he had been brought into the world, and his lack of the doe's colostrum. As yet, we had no tangible proof that any of these incidents were related to this dramatic reversal in his health. Although we explored every avenue to heal him, and to encourage him to eat, Navajo responded to none of them. We increased the antibiotics as the fever became more pronounced, but he slowly weakened, closed his eyes for the last time, and died peacefully as he slept.

A wildlife lab necropsy revealed the cause of death to be a bacterial infection, Navel Ill, a term used when the umbilical cord is not properly cleaned, or when an object, such as the contaminated knife, introduces bacteria, which passes through the navel and into the animal's vital organs. This slow progressing disease allowed him to have his few extra days of life. The pathologist also noted an injury to Navajo's undeveloped rumen. This small stomach could not expand as his body attempted to grow. We assumed the injury to his rumen was caused when the doe was thrown by the truck.

Since that sad incident, I have had other experiences with pregnant does that were hit by cars. These animals don't understand the potential danger of an oncoming vehicle. Too often drivers speed recklessly down our twisting mountain roads unmindful of the strategically placed "Deer Crossing" signs warning them to slow down and keep a watchful eye out for unwary wildlife. Each time I arrive at these tragic scenes, I wonder at the callousness of humans who don't stop to aid the suffering animal they have injured.

One morning, in answer to an emergency call, I hastened to a remote mountain spot where a huge injured doe lay upright in a deep ditch by the roadside. Realizing I couldn't lift this alert, struggling deer alone, I phoned for help from a nearby neighbor's home. It would be some time before the Animal Control officer could reach me on this steep canyon road. As I waited around the bend, out of the doe's sight, a friend drove by and stopped to ask if I had car trouble. After hearing my problem, she insisted on helping me get the deer into my truck without further delay. The two of us managed to shift the terrified, protesting doe onto a blanket.

As we tried to lift her out of the ditch, a man dressed in business clothes pulled his car alongside and jumped out to help. More by sheer will than strength, we hoisted the struggling animal into the back of my camper. After promising to let my two helpers know the outcome, I rushed the doe, by now in shock, to the back entrance of the vet clinic. Dr. Patton checked her condition and ran to gather his equipment from the clinic. Without moving the doe, he administered the anesthesia and performed a Caesarean section. Immediately he passed the newborn to his technician, who dashed into the clinic to place the tiny creature in a respirator. The fawn died within minutes. Dr. Patton returned to the truck once more to euthanize the badly crushed doe, who had never regained consciousness. To my knowledge, no accident-related fawn delivered by Caesarean section has ever lived to maturity. We continue to try, hoping that one day a miracle fawn will survive. I think back in wonder to Navajo's few short weeks of life and marvel that he ever lived at all.

Over the years, the television documentary of Navajo and his unusual birth continues to be aired. Each time I glimpse the innocent deep brown eyes gazing directly into the camera, his bright spots gleaming so vividly on his red-brown hair, and his wobbly attempts to balance on his spindly legs, my heart aches at the shortness of his life.

17

Cinnamon

As the shot rings out, a Black Bear crashes to the ground. Holding the rifle aimed toward his prey, the poacher heads in the direction of his shot. "Hey, B.J.," he shouts, "come here a minute. Look what we've got."

"A bear, I hope," laughs his partner, as he pushes through the dense brush.

"And then some," answers Todd, pointing to the large female bear lying prone by a fallen log. Behind her still body crouches a tiny six-pound cub, her eyes large with fear.

"Just great, Todd. Now what do we do? Might just as well shoot it, too. What else is there to do with it?"

"I guess it's pretty damning evidence, huh?" Todd replies. "But we could take it back to camp and see what the gang says."

"I don't get it. You shoot the mom, out of season, right from the logging trail, and don't raise a hair. Now you want to take this cub back to camp. I say shoot it now, before we find ourselves in a real mess."

The two men gut the bear, fling the parts of value into a sack and stand up. Pulling rags from their pockets, they wipe their hands, and throw the rags into the brush. "Ain't it funny how those people will pay us a fortune for this stuff? They swear it has all kinds of special powers. Makes them feel real good, I hear," B.J. said.

"I don't much care what they use it for," Todd answers brusquely. He slings his rifle over his shoulder, tucks the cub under his arm, and heads back toward the truck while his partner follows carrying the sack.

B.J. climbs behind the wheel, muttering about "stupidity." They jolt over ruts and rocks, through miles of clear-cut forest area, slowly moving in the direction of the logging camp. The cub clings tightly to the burly shoulder of the poacher who had so recently shot her mother.

"How was the hunt, guys?" calls one of the loggers as the partners pull into camp. "Bring back dinner?"

"Better than that," Todd laughs. "Got us a mascot. We'll sure have a lot of fun with this little gal."

The men gather around the terrified cub, scratching her behind the ears, passing her from hand to hand. "Where'd you find her?" one asks.

"Strangest thing," Todd replies casually. "We heard a rustle in the brush, and out pops this scared little bear cub. Something must have gotten the mom. We never did find her. I told B.J. you guys would love to have her around after a hard day's work. What d'ya say?" B.J., head down, walks quickly away toward the out house.

"Well, no one would ever know she was here, now would they?" says one.

"We could keep her in a pen while we're gone and let her run loose when we're here," another comments.

"Yeah, that'd be a blast. She could go free right here once she gets too rough to handle," remarks a third. "In fact, she's pretty feisty right now. I read in a huntin' magazine somewhere that bears are only about a half pound when they're born. Figure this one to be about six weeks old?"

"Close enough."

"It's settled, then," Todd smiles. "We'll need a bottle and maybe some goat milk, or whatever. Someone find out, without being too obvious. Okay?"

The cage is built quickly, and Cinnamon settles into the logging camp.

*

The old farmer is suspicious. "All of a sudden, over a bottle of beer, there's too many casual questions about what bear cubs eat," he mutters to himself on the drive home from the local gathering spot. "If there's a cub back at that camp, and it survives, it will grow up tame and dangerous. Hate to see it get shot just because someone made a pet out of it."

One night, after a few more bear remarks, the old man feels even more uneasy. "Think I'd better give Sal a call, just to be on the safe side. No harm done if there's no cub."

Sal Provost, the local game warden, receives calls from the northeastern section of California's Region One. Problems overlap from county to county and the wardens pass along the information to each other. Early Monday morning Sal straps on his pistol and reaches for his jacket. The June weather is still brisk in the foothills. He grabs for the ringing phone as he passes by the desk, "Warden Provost," he answers.

"Hi, Sal. Jim Jenning here," says the farmer. "I keep hearing little remarks that make me think there may be a cub being kept at the logger's camp. Thought I'd just run the information by you for whatever you might think it's worth."

"The logging camp over on the old spur road? That's just on the edge of my territory. Bear country, for sure. I'll look into it. Thanks for the tip, Jim."

Sal picks up his partner, Tony Galdo, and then drives by the logging camp. All is quiet. The loggers are out on the job. The wardens can see one side of a strongly built chain link pen leading into an open shed. "I'd say a dog would be out barking a warning by now. So what do you suppose is in that big enclosure?" Sal remarks.

"A bear? A little Black Bear cub?" laughs Tony.

"Let's get a search warrant and check it out."

A few evenings later the loggers are scattered around the camp preparing for their evening event, the good hot meal they look forward to with enthusiasm. Plenty of solid down-home cooking, pots of hot coffee, and, usually big chunks of freshly baked pie. The cook is good and well paid. Cinnamon bounces between the men like a pup.

Everyone freezes as the California Department of Fish and Game vehicle pulls into the compound. The two wardens step from the truck and stoop to scratch the small cub who runs over to greet them.

Finally, after a few questions by the wardens, and direct glances from the loggers, Todd admits bringing the cub into camp. He keeps to the story he had told the loggers. B.J.'s uneasy *I-told-you-so* expression clearly shows his complicity. Although the wardens are aware that poaching is going on in the area, until now they have had no clue as to who these criminals might be. Now that they are alerted, they will keep close watch on, and eventually trip up, these particular men. The bear pen disproves Todd's statement that the cub isn't being held illegally. And he can't deny that although the cub has been with them for several weeks, no attempt has been made to turn it over to the Department. A citation is issued to Todd for the illegal possession of wildlife. The wardens tuck Cinnamon into a transport cage and head back to headquarters.

*

Born in a den during semi-hibernation, Black Bear cubs are blind, slightly furred, and measure about eight inches in length.

These solitary animals may be seen, both day and night, on their range of approximately fifteen miles in a habitat of forest and wooded mountains. They have a keen sense of smell, moderate hearing and poor vision. California Black Bears, our smallest native North American bear, average one-half pound at birth. They grow to their maximum weight in five years, from 120 pounds for small females, to 350 pounds for the larger males. Cubs grow rapidly, and within a few weeks follow the female out of the den. The mother does not mate while nursing her cub through its first year. Therefore, she only gives birth every two years. If food becomes scarce, that period can be extended for as long as four years. Nature keeps the bear population well under control.

Although these omnivorous animals are basically vegetarians, they can find nutrition in almost any organic food. Their diet may consist of greens, leaves, tubers, nuts, fruit, twigs and bugs, vegetables and honey, as well as larvae, insects, grubs and beetles, eggs, carrion and an occasional small mammal. They excel at fishing.

*

According to the Department of Fish and Game, once a bear has been kept in captivity, the chance of returning it back into the wild is slim. This leaves only three options to consider. Destroy the cub, keep it as an exhibit, or send it to a specialized bear rehabilitation center. One other method has been successfully tried by experienced biologists, but the circumstances must be ideal. A newborn cub may be placed in the den of a lactating female for adoption. But this is not an option for this confiscated cub since it is not newly born.

An article in our local newspaper alerted me to the plight of this female cub. The article stated that the cub had been placed in the care of a wildlife center whose resident bear had died. This facility had the only available cage in the area, and placing Cinnamon with them seemed like a reasonable answer to the warden's immediate problem.

To my horror, the article described in detail the manner in which Cinnamon was being treated. "We feed her dog food, cottage cheese and fruit," the animal director told the reporter. "She will live in our bear enclosure, which is a twenty-by-twenty-foot concrete pen containing a cinder block den." She went on to explain, "I know it sounds mean, but a good part of Cinnamon's training will involve keeping her fearful of humans. Our staff members yell and growl, bang metal lids together, and kick the sides of the cage as they go by. We hardly ever see her because she hides in the den." This director's method of handling the cub was irresponsible and unnecessarily cruel.

I envisioned this eleven-week-old bear huddling in the cold cinder block structure, alone and terrified, afraid to come out into the air and sunshine. Aware that other California Black Bears were shipped north to a Washington specialized bear facility, I could see no reason for Cinnamon to live under the conditions which were described in this newspaper article.

In past years Bruin, a male Black Bear, had been confined in this same cage for twenty years under stressful conditions. He died a lingering and painful death from arthritis caused by his life in this unnatural habitat. Therefore, I questioned the motives behind this center's actions. Since Bruin proved to be such a great attraction and brought them money and fame, what would prevent this facility from claiming that Cinnamon was so badly imprinted by the loggers and by her exposure to the public, that she could not be released.

I wrote to the Board of Directors of the facility where Cinnamon lived. I reminded them of the specialized bear facility where this cub could be raised with other bears in a natural outdoor environment and where she would be provided with proper nourishment. If this concrete cage was the best they could provide and a better alternative existed, why, I asked, was Cinnamon still there? I urged them to make arrangements for the transfer as quickly as possible. I pleaded with them to think about the well-being of the cub. I received no reply.

My next step, a letter to the Department of Fish and Game, explained my concerns. Once again, I asked that the bear be transferred. The Department sent a warden to investigate. The center convinced the warden that all was well with the little bear. Since all he saw was the bear in the cage, and wasn't aware of the terror this cub was subjected to every day, his report stated that the bear was in good condition and should stay at the center.

This decision came to me as a powerful blow. The bear needed help. Since she was so young, it was reasonable to think that she could be prepared for a life in the wild. I decided to appeal to the public for help with the situation. As a result of my letter to the newspaper, over thirty people wrote letters of protest to the Department. Radio and TV stations gave the story further publicity.

I received a call from Louann Billings, an executive of the wildlife center where Cinnamon lived. "What are you trying to do to us?" She screamed in my ear.

"I'm just trying to get that cub transferred," I explained. "I wrote to your organization, but since you chose not to reply, you left me with no other choice." She asked if we could meet to talk. Pleased, I invited her to stop by my home.

Louann proved to be a charming, attractive person, but it soon became apparent that although she worked in an executive capacity at the center, she knew nothing about wildlife or their needs. She did know, however, that bears create a good deal of public interest and that having one at the facility would be a real moneymaker.

"You don't seem to understand what the future of this cub will be," I said. "You're new to the organization and never saw Bruin during his final years, limping in agony from arthritis brought on by twenty years of pacing on concrete floors and sleeping in a damp, cold cinder block den. Bruin never touched the earth, never swam in a stream, fished, or pulled berries from a vine. Is this what you want for Cinnamon?"

"Would it help if I told you the animal director has been fired and the cub is no longer being terrorized?" Louann replied, evading my question.

"Yes, it does help, but it's not enough. In twenty years you and I will be gone, but Cinnamon will still be alone in her twenty-foot cage. No one will remember, or care, that at one time Cinnamon was a small, eleven-week-old cub, a good candidate for a life of freedom. Why should she be denied living with her own species, mating, giving birth and nurturing her young?"

"She'll have a long sheltered life..."

"Perhaps she might live longer in captivity. Nature is hard and exacting. But this is not a valid reason to imprison an animal that is genetically programed to be wild. Don't you see, Louann?"

We talked for more than an hour. I could not make her understand how important the life of this one bear cub was. Louann rose to leave. As we walked to her car, I said, "I'm glad you stopped by so that we could talk. However, since nothing has been resolved, I still intend to continue with my effort to have Cinnamon transferred."

Louann smiled vaguely and replied, "Yes, I'm sure you will try." But her body language projected a different message. As she reached to pat me on the shoulder, she may as well have said, "For all the good it will do you."

I laughed as I watched her drive down the hill and thought, so the irresistible force has met the immovable object. It helped to have met my adversary in person.

Louann issued a press release in which she altered the facts by claiming that a group of animal rights activists were trying to undermine their prestigious facility and force the transfer of the young bear. Their organization did not think this action would be in the best interest of Cinnamon, the release said.

The following day Louann drove to the headquarters of the Department of Fish and Game for a talk with the director. After Louann's visit the director called me to reaffirm that the Department was satisfied with the present arrangements. He told me plainly that this cub was not my problem, and he suggested that I should leave the future of Cinnamon in their hands.

*

Hoping to at least be able to improve the cub's diet, I phoned an information center where wild animal diets were kept on file. The woman who answered my call misunderstood my questioning and reported to the Department that she suspected that I had a bear in my possession.

Shortly after her report two wardens appeared at my door. In reply to my greeting one warden asked abruptly, "Do you have a bear cub here, Maggie?" I knew at once what had prompted the visit. I explained that my call had been made on behalf of the cub at the wildlife facility.

"Nevertheless, we'll have to check it out," she replied.

"Fine. Where would you like to look first, inside the house, or out in the fawn enclosures?"

The warden smiled sheepishly and said, "I told headquarters you would never risk losing your permit over something so idiotic. But you understand that we do have to respond to this type of report."

As we browsed through the fawn pens, I said, "I would certainly turn a bear cub in to the Department if I got a call for one. Why would I want to keep it? I have all I can handle caring for fawns."

*

Word spread about Cinnamon's plight. A Wildlife Protection officer from state headquarters called to say he agreed that Cinnamon must be transferred before she became much older. We discussed how highly susceptible Cinnamon was to infectious diseases from both humans and other wildlife in her existing environment. We spoke of the lack of adequate space for her to exercise, her need for soil to walk on so her paws could grow normally, and the importance of socialization with other bears. The officer promised to see that a transfer came through by the end of the week. Expecting quick action, I slept well that night. When a week passed and nothing happened, I called our local headquarters to inquire about the delay. They assured me that this office had received no order for a transfer. I left a phone message for the Wildlife Protection officer at state headquarters. He never replied.

So, once again, I turned to the public for help. This time, animal rights organizations and other concerned groups took up the cause. I located an interested party who offered to cover the cost of the cub's transfer, whether by plane or by truck. Public pressure built against those who held Cinnamon captive.

Over three months had passed since Cinnamon was picked up by the loggers. Time was running out. Before long the authorities would decide that this bear had been in captivity too long for a successful release. Early one morning I answered the phone to hear a young woman speaking in a quiet voice, "Maggie, I work as a volunteer at the wildlife facility that has the cub. There are two wardens here. They tagged Cinnamon. What do you think that's all about?"

Tears flowed as I answered softly, "It means she is being transferred. Thank you for letting me know."

I immediately called Dennis Stone, a newspaper columnist who had been supportive throughout the crisis. I told him what I had learned. "Dennis, will you call the wildlife facility to see if you can find out where and when the cub is being transferred?"

Dennis called back quickly. "Cinnamon is already on her way to the bear rehabilitation center in Washington. Now that's what I call good news!" In the next issue of the paper large print at the top of his column shouted "HEY, HEY, HEY BEAR CUB'S ON HER WAY."

Over a year later I attended a wildlife conference in Southern California. Matt Simon, the director of the Washington bear center was one of the featured speakers. After his talk I walked up to shake his hand, not intending to mention my past connection with Cinnamon. I put out my hand and said, "Hi, I'm Maggie McKenzie from Fawn Rescue in Northern California."

He smiled as he took my hand and said, "Yes, I know who you are." Then I felt free to ask, "How's Cinnamon?" His eyes lit up. "Cinnamon was released this spring in a remote part of the National Park from where she came."

Happiness is an orphaned Black Bear cub regaining her freedom.

18

An Occasional Buck

Injured adult deer are nearly impossible to treat. They won't hesitate to rip apart any vet clinic, not to mention any vet who dares attempt to help them. Raised in the wild, deer do not adapt to captivity. Their inborn fear of man forces them to bash and batter themselves against any enclosure as they fight to escape. Although the bones in young animals heal quickly, breaks in an older deer cannot be mended, and like a horse, they must be euthanized.

Fawn Rescue is not Deer Rescue and is only equipped to handle fawns. Nevertheless, I continue to receive calls to rescue adult deer. When I refer these callers to Animal Control, they insist that the injured animal is a fawn. I arrive at the scene to find a badly injured full-grown deer, and most often Animal Control must still be contacted, which only prolongs the animal's agony until they arrive. However, when the injury is not too severe, the animal sometimes can be saved.

One typically foggy June morning I awakened to the jarring ring of the phone. As I made an effort to gather my thoughts, Mr. Garrett described the buck he had found lying outside his gate. Although hit by a car, the unconscious deer was still alive. Mr. Garrett pulled the injured animal into his yard, and now he asked me if I would come at once so he could get on to work.

"I can't possibly handle a full-grown buck alone, Mr. Garrett. You'll need to call Animal Control. They're under contract with the county to handle this kind of situation."

"I don't want him shot. He looks as though he's just stunned. There's no blood, no broken bones," he explained. "I'm only about three miles from you. Will you just take a look? I'll wait to help you get it into your truck if you come right away," he persisted.

"If you wait, I'll come," I promised. No heavy traffic clogged the highway at this early hour. But fog, opaque and shimmering, hung in the low spots, slowing me down and giving me the illusion of being encased in a milk bottle. As I turned into the Garretts' driveway, I saw the forked-horned buck lying inert on the grass. Mr. Garrett and I struggled to move the hefty, muscular deer onto a blanket, then lift him into the back of the camper.

I handed my helper a brochure and waved a hurried good by. "Call me at this number tonight, and I'll let you know how the big guy is doing," I told him. I reasoned that by the time I reversed my direction and drove north to Dr. Patton's clinic, it would be just opening. But when I pulled into the driveway, no lights shown through the windows of the building. I parked by the back door, knowing he would arrive soon. As though on cue, the doctor pulled up beside me with a questioning smile.

After taking a quick peek at the unmoving buck, we labored to carry him into emergency. In our haste to help, we focused entirely on the needs of the animal, and failed to consider the havoc this robust wild creature could create if it suddenly regained consciousness. Obviously, these were the early years of our work together with wildlife. Although the doctor had helped with ill and injured fawns many times before, this buck would provide the first in a series of well remembered lessons in our work together over the coming years.

The absorbed young vet examined the buck thoroughly, then said, "It appears to be head trauma, and I'd say he'll be fine. I'll just give him an injection of cortisone, and we'll take it from there. Not much else we can do for him." Hardly had the injection been given, than the slightly dazed buck opened his eyes, stared directly into the brilliant lights a few inches above his massive head, and groaned.

"Whoa, fellow," said the startled doctor. "That's a little too fast. We'd better get you out of here while I still have a clinic. Perhaps we should have settled him first, then given him his magic recovery shot." He shouted for his assistant, and they desperately worked to move the rapidly recovering buck into a kennel area behind the clinic. They placed him in a large dog run, propped him up on his sternum, and backed off, carefully closing the door of the enclosure behind them.

Knowing my fawns would be wondering why I was late with their breakfast, I thanked Dr. Patton, and rushed home to feed the young ones. I planned on calling the clinic to check on our buck a little later in the morning. I finished feeding nine fawns and a few squirrels, heated my morning coffee, then sank into a chair, hoping for a few minutes' break. A break was not meant to be. I reached across the desk to pick up the phone on the first insistent ring. Dr. Patton's deep laugh sounded in my ear. "Just thought you'd want to know, Maggie. I went out to check on our wild friend just now. There he stood, stiff legged and defiant, with his head lowered and his ears laid back. That threatening look in those piercing eyes told me he would charge any second. I swung open the gate very cautiously, stood far back out of his path, and wished the big guy good luck."

"Wow. I bet he didn't think long about what to do next," I remarked with delight.

"You're right. He never hesitated," the vet answered. "He trotted out through that gate, across the creek, and on up into

Annadel Park. Lucky for him the park was so handy. He didn't seem in a special hurry once he was free. He never looked back. What a beautiful sight. What a reward. I wish you could have seen him, Maggie."

"It's enough that he made it."

*

The reflection of Hannah's headlights bounced against the bedroom drapes, disturbing, but not quite awakening me from a deep sleep. My husband opened the window and turned on the outside light as her van pulled to a stop beside the garage. She jumped out to run toward our front door. "I'll get Maggie. She'll know what to do," I heard Hannah say to her companions who waited in the van. Fully awake by now, I recognized my friend's voice. Quickly, my husband and I pulled on our robes as we made our way out the door. The group gathered around the open door of the van. Inside lay a large yearling just beginning to stir. Before making introductions or asking questions, the men efficiently transferred the young spike into the back of my covered pickup. The frightened, scuffed-up buck kicked during the transfer, but quieted down once the hatch closed behind him.

Hannah introduced us to the young couple, Sally and Bill, then she recounted the story of their night's adventure. They were returning from a movie in Santa Rosa, she told us. As they drove toward home on twisting, winding Bennett Valley Road, they swerved to avoid hitting the body of a deer lying sprawled on the road. Agreeing that it created a serious hazard, they stopped to move the body out of traffic's way. The deer, illuminated in their headlights, moved slightly as they approached. Another car stopped just then to offer assistance and a blanket, and together, they managed to lift the dazed young deer into Hannah's van.

Hannah insisted on heading directly to Fawn Rescue with their patient, assuring her friends that it would be all right to do so. Spending precious time looking for a phone would only delay his treatment, she said.

The rescuers shined their flashlights into the camper while I examined his torn and bleeding antlers. Spirals of shredded velvet curled down over his eyes. "He looks messy," I said. "But that seems to be the only injury he has. I'll give him medication for head trauma and hope there are no internal injuries. He can rest in the truck for the night and be ready for his ride to the vet in the morning, or back home if he's recovered."

"What do you think, Maggie, will he make it?" Hannah asked anxiously.

"I'd say he has a good chance, but I'll call you in the morning and let you know either way," I answered, stifling a yawn.

"Let's all get some sleep. Babies to feed in a few hours." The group left, and we sank gratefully back into bed.

I awakened refreshed. The sun shone brightly in a cloudless sky. A good omen. I walked toward the camper enthusiastically. At a deep level, I somehow knew that this time I would find our visiting yearling on his feet and ready to go. From a distance I could see him gazing alertly out the side window. Backing silently away, I scurried to answer the phone ringing inside the garage. In answer to her query, I told Hannah the happy news. "He's been given a second chance," she cried with joy. Without hesitation she accepted my invitation to accompany me on the release and point out the spot the little buck would recognize as home.

We traveled at a slow pace along the route Hannah remembered so well. Suddenly she said, "It's very near here, I'm sure. This curve straightens out into a long stretch of road. It looks different in daylight, but yes, there's the fence. Pull over anywhere close to it."

I backed the truck, containing the eager buck, against a half open, derelict gate which opened onto a browning field of high weeds. I turned off the motor and we stepped down onto the roadside. Just then, from far up on the hill, a small group of deer emerged from the woods as though in expectation of our arrival. "The welcoming committee. Can't you just feel the energy between them?"

laughed Hannah in delight. She positioned her camera to record the unusual event, while I walked to the back of the truck, lifted the hatch, and let down the tailgate. The yearling, filled with renewed vigor, stood poised and ready to leap. He bounded out, strongly and surely, into the open field. His herd trotted nimbly toward him, touched noses in recognition, then as a group, turned in an instant to lead him off into the trees and home.

*

On my next trip to Dr. Patton's with an injured, full-grown deer, we didn't even consider carrying the enormous buck into his clinic filled with waiting clients. Our previous forked-horn experience remained impressed on our minds. This three-point buck remained safely in the camper where the vet came out to examine him, give him steroids for the head injury, and wave me on my way. "We've done our best, Maggie," he smiled. "The rest is up to him. Everything looks intact, but I'd say he received a hefty blow to the head. Better get him back to Fawn Rescue before he comes out of it."

Once at the fawn facility I guided the groggy deer into a lower pen that had a gate which opened into the woods. Within an hour, the buck stood steady on his feet, but it was apparent that all of his senses were gone. He stared sightlessly into space. He made no attempt to move at my approach, nor did he turn his head in my direction or twitch his mammoth ears. I offered him water and food, neither of which he smelled, even though I held them directly under his nose. When I called Dr. Patton for advice, he suggested giving the ailing buck ten days to overcome the trauma. He warned me that getting enough nourishment into his huge frame would be my biggest problem.

The disoriented buck lay under the shelter of a heavily ladened apple tree. He showed no desire to sample the ripened fruit, usually an irresistible temptation for a deer. I sat beside him, placed his antlered head on my lap, wrapped soft wild grape and oak leaves around small bits of grain, then pushed it into his mouth. He chewed willingly and swallowed hungrily as I fed him. How enormous the head of this three-point buck seemed, compared to the fawns I usually held. I offered him pieces of chopped apple and bites of alfalfa until he turned his head away and refused more. Then I dribbled a small but steady stream of water into his mouth for as long as he continued to swallow.

The third day I found him standing solidly under the apple tree, in full control of his sturdy frame and nibbling with enthusiasm on the leaves. Our first victory.

His sense of taste and smell were back in working order. I walked close to freshen his water, but my presence didn't disturb him. A long way to go, I thought.

On day seven of his recovery, his ears twitched and his head turned toward me as I crept silently near his pen. I stopped and stood quietly. He tensed and listened. I sensed his wariness. So we're no longer friends, I thought, or were we ever?

The next morning, the eighth day after the accident, there he stood, alert and threatening. He looked up the stairway, watching me intently, as I took one slow step at a time down toward the gate, His powerful stance strongly sent out the message: he was totally whole and ready to take his place in his wild world once more. I continued to descend cautiously. His eyes never left me, nor did a muscle move on his elegant, sleek frame. Close now, I quietly pulled back the gate, then retreated once more to the top of the stairs. The wary buck gazed inquiringly at the open gate and then up at me sitting in the distance, far out of his trail. In full control of his destiny now, the buck, antlers held high, walked toward the exit. He took one precautionary step through the opening where he stood fixed and calm, gazing down into the thick stand of oak. Then, as I watched spellbound, with deliberate, measured steps, he vanished into the brush like a magnificent woodland spirit.

19

The Chase

Early fall weekends entice families to visit our public parks for the last remaining days of picnicking and recreation. This warm Sunday morning I received several urgent calls, all reporting the same fawn. This male fawn had wandered into the picnic area to feed on the freshly fallen acorns from an ancient Valley Oak. The oak's massive limbs spread wide over a popular corner table. The public, loaded with picnic baskets, recreation equipment, children and toys, streamed in as soon as the gates swung open. The trapped young deer became an immediate attraction for energetic children who wanted to touch and play with him. Chased round and round the fenced section, the small buck suddenly found the exit gate. Then, in a panic, he turned left onto busy Summerfield Road instead of turning right, which would have led him into the wooded hills and home.

Brakes screamed, adults attempted to herd the disoriented fawn back into the park, but he dashed through traffic and into a housing subdivision on the opposite side of the street. By the time I arrived, the frightened young animal had traveled several blocks in the wrong direction. I parked by the curb, grabbed my blanket and headed toward a side street, hoping to cut him off in the school yard where he had vanished.

As I emerged, running full tilt up the main thoroughfare with the fawn streaking a half block ahead of me, a tall, blond young man swung his car into a U-turn and came to a hasty halt. He ran along side of me to ask what was going on. "I'm Kenny Hessel. What can I do to help?" he asked. Never slowing my pace, I explained my rescue mission. Not waiting to hear more, Kenny picked up speed and raced past me on the trail of the wayward fawn.

Into the school yard they flew. The exhausted little buck threw himself under a hedge trying to escape the persistent young man. Kenny stood guard waiting for me to catch up. "I think we've got him," he shouted with elation. "You go from that side, and I'll take this one." As we closed in on the fawn from either end, he made a frantic lunge through the center of the hedge, and the chase was on again. Off he ran, full speed across the grassy school yard, careening around the corner and into a residential street, with Kenny hot on his trail and me bringing up a distant rear.

The fawn cut through private lawns, across flower beds, over low fences at a speed and agility that belied his age and size. Finally he ran into a yard surrounded with a high, deteriorating wooden fence. The yard was covered with lumber, bags of concrete, piles of gravel, and various sized pipes. Kenny said cheerfully, "This time we've got him, for sure. There's no place he can go." The fawn flailed about in the building material and cut his leg on a sharp piece of lumber as it flew out from under him. Blood splattered on the pile of wood. Material scattered everywhere, as we tried to climb over it to capture the frenzied young deer. As Kenny grabbed for him from behind, the fawn flung himself, screaming into the fence. A rotted board gave way, and the small animal fled through the hole and into the yard beyond, which led him onto the next street.

Undaunted, Kenny dashed out of the yard and disappeared around the corner. This was my last glimpse of both animal and man. I ran back to my truck and cruised the residential neighborhood, stopping to ask Sunday strollers if they had seen either a fawn or a running young man.

"A fawn? Around here? The only deer I ever see are up in the park. They never come down here, lady," one man answered, as he shrugged and glanced with raised eyebrows at his companion.

I spent the next fifteen minutes searching for Kenny and the little buck. Finally, deciding to end my futile search, I headed toward home, hoping someone else would spot the wayward wild creature and call me.

The phone rang as I pulled into the garage. "Is this Fawn Rescue?" a woman's voice asked. "A young man is crouched in my back yard holding a fawn with a bloody leg. They both look in bad shape. The man asked me to try to find a lady who rescues fawns. He didn't know your name. I called the Humane Society, and they gave me this number. I hope it's the right place."

"Do you live near Howarth Park?" I asked, hopefully.

"Yes, about six blocks down. Why?"

"Well," I laughed, "there can only be one young man with an injured fawn in that neighborhood. Tell Kenny I'll be right there, and to hold on to that fawn. Give me your address."

The woman waited in front of her house to lead me into her pristine backyard where Kenny sat holding the frazzled little buck in his arms. Sweat poured down Kenny's grinning face and onto his blood-splattered shirt. His blue eyes gleamed in triumph. He stood up to carry the trembling, exhausted fawn and lay him gently on the carpeted floor in the back of my truck. "Take good care of him and let me know how he is," he said.

"Kenny, you have my undying gratitude," I said. "I've never seen anyone stick to a goal like you did today."

"I just couldn't stop. I knew he would be killed if I didn't capture him. He's too young to find his way back into the park. That's a long way from here. Besides, he has that bad leg."

"You deserve the animal medal of honor," I laughed.

"What I really would like, if it's at all possible, is to go with you when he's released. And I'd also like to become a volunteer to help with calls from this area. I live just down the street."

"I could use help when I have to decide which of several calls is the most urgent. Come out to Fawn Rescue, see what I do, then we'll talk about it."

The little buck's leg healed, and two weeks later I called Kenny to help with the release. We cornered the protesting, still wild animal, placed him in an airline carrier, and drove fifteen miles to the park. Kenny, an avid hiker, knew of a back entrance that would lead us directly into the area from where the fawn had originally come. We parked close by the path to the woods. Then, with one of us on either side of the carrier, we walked together, carrying the enclosed unruly deer up the steep path to a high meadow. We set the carrier facing into a deep ravine that would lead him home to join his family. Kenny reached down, unlatched and opened the carrier door. The small buck leaped out, hesitated only an instant, then crashed through the brush and down a familiar path to freedom.

A gentle breeze stirred. Kenny and I hiked the long route back, enjoying the sun on our backs. We stopped to gaze upward at our first sighting of Canada geese migrating in V-formation, their deep, musical honk echoing in our ears.

20
Sky Show

A local newspaper published an interesting article alerting its readers to an unusual heat and lightning display to be seen in the northern sky that night. The best viewing spots were listed. I felt tempted to drive to the nearby top of Sonoma Mountain for a quick look, but after an exhausting day of wildlife work, a good night's rest seemed more important. The next morning would come all too soon when eight hungry fawns would be waiting eagerly by the feeders to compete for their first bottles of warm formula. I must also be alert and ready for the emergency calls I would surely get this early part of June.

I went to bed reluctantly, thinking about the exciting sky show that would carry on without me this time. Just before 2 a.m., the shrill ring of the phone awakened me from a deep sleep. I stood bare footed and groggy as I listened to a man apologizing for the lateness of the call. The young man identified himself as Bernie Paulson, and urgently explained his problem. "I saw a large herd of deer grazing in the field, as I sat in my car up on Sonoma Mountain," he began. "Maybe I spooked them, because, just as I started my engine to leave, they decided to bolt across the road in front of me." He continued to say that he braked at once, and avoided hitting any of them, but one trailing fawn ran head on into the side of his car. "I jumped out to find the little guy sprawled on the road, totally unconscious. I wrapped him in my car blanket and laid him on the back seat to get him home so I could find help. The Sheriff's Department gave me your phone number. They said you rescue fawns. I'm sure glad somebody does. I don't know what to do with him."

"How's he doing now?" I asked. "Is he still in your car?"

"That's the biggest part of my problem," he chuckled. "He began to wake up in my car. You can bet I picked up speed when I saw him begin to move. I got him home, pulled him out of the car, and barely managed to carry him into my back yard. I'll tell you, he's strong. I think he'll be fine."

"Sounds like he's ready to go home. Is there any way you can take him back where you found him?" I asked hopefully.

"No way at all. That's why I'm calling you at this time of night. He'd tear my car apart, and me with it, I'm afraid," he replied. He's out in the yard charging around hitting against the wooden fence. I don't want him to hurt himself again."

"And he will," I assured him. "Give me your address. I'll hurry." I dressed quickly and sped down our country road to Highway 12, heading toward the far west side of Santa

Rosa. Luckily, at that time of night, traffic was light and most of the stoplights shone a steady green. Bernie stood outside his house waving a flashlight when I turned onto his street. As we entered the gate, the fawn headed toward the corner of the yard away from us. "Good, he'll hide under that bush, and I can capture him easily with my blanket," I said. "You stand on this side, in case he shoots out from behind."

The fawn ran for the cover of the bush, as expected. Giving him no chance to change his mind, I threw the blanket over him and straddled his body. A few branches of the bush crackled and broke in the struggle. "I'll need your help getting him into the truck," I said. "Sorry about your bush."

Bernie shrugged in answer to my apology, then together we ran toward the front of the house with the frightened, fully alert animal kicking and screaming inside the blanket.

"I've never heard the cry of a fawn before," Bernie remarked, as we thrust him into the camper and slammed the door. "It's awful. Like the bleat of a goat, yet more powerful and compelling."

"It's a sound you'll never forget," I answered. "It's so seldom heard, and so unnerving that it sinks deep into the psyche."

The young buck quieted down once he was free in the back of the camper, and my attention turned to the next important step. It was crucial to the survival of the fawn that he be returned to the exact spot where he had been picked up. "He must be reunited with his family, and even a quarter of a mile can make a difference to one this young," I explained to my helper. I worried about finding the precise location on that mountain road in the dark, and questioned Bernie apprehensively. "Are there any specific landmarks I should look for?"

He shook his head emphatically. "You'll never find it without me, Maggie. It's all open country up there. I'm as interested in a happy ending as you are, so follow me. I'll guide you up to the spot where it happened."

Grateful for his support, I slid into the Fawnmobile and made a U-turn on the deserted street to fall in behind Bernie's small black sports car. We drove east into Santa Rosa, then south through Rohnert Park. Finally reaching the foothills, we began the incline to the top of Sonoma Mountain. A full moon lighted the way through shimmering brown fields on both sides of the road. I caught a flash of brilliant lightning streaking across the sky to my left. Near the top, Bernie signaled with his blinker that we were approaching our destination. We pulled to a stop just off the road and stepped out of our vehicles. Bernie motioned silently to the herd of deer still grazing in the high field above us to the right. I slowly opened the back of the camper, and without a moment's hesitation, the small buck leaped out, ran toward the front of our vehicles, jumped a small ditch, and stooped low to squeeze under an opening in the fence that ran the length of the road. At home once more, he knew each step of the way to the spot where his mother and the others were feeding. As he reached her side, the doe turned her head to nudge him gently in recognition, then returned to her grazing. The fawn contentedly nibbled along with the others, never glancing in our direction.

Bernie and I stood side by side enjoying the moonlit view on this unusually warm and sultry night. "What were you doing up here at such a late hour?" I asked.

The young man laughed. "You'll think I'm crazy. I drove up to watch the sky show. I'm an avid skywatcher. Sometimes the sunsets toward Bodega Bay are outstanding from here. Tonight was spectacular and well worth losing a few hours sleep."

As if on cue, vivid lightning zigzagged repeatedly across the cloudless sky. "I have you to thank for getting me up here to see this," I said, as the sky continued to flash with dazzling light. "I thought of coming, but decided against it. Now I'm here in spite of my decision. You're right. It's well worth the trip."

"We are each in debt to the other, then. You turned my horrifying experience into a privilege I'll never forget," he answered.

We continued to talk for a few more minutes before shaking hands in farewell. Bernie turned his car to head west down the mountain road. I continued up over the crest of Sonoma Mountain and down the eastern slope toward Kenwood and the Valley of the Moon. The following day, as I attended my duties around Fawn Rescue in a sleepy haze, I carried with me pleasant memories of a caring young man, a successful release, and a spectacular sky show.

Afterward

Seasons pass, and the years fly swiftly by. Fawn Rescue continues to accept each wildlife challenge as it arises. One day my work will end. Would that I were clairvoyant, having the keen perception to know in future years who will be here to carry the torch.

Author Profile

As Founder and Director of Wildlife Fawn Rescue, a wildlife rehabilitation facility in Northern California, Marjorie (Maggie) McKenzie Davis has been rescuing fawns in distress for more than a decade, treating at least 100 injured or orphaned fawns each year. She runs the only wildlife organization in California that specializes solely in deer. Her work echoes Chief Seattle's belief: *What is man without the beasts? If all the beasts were gone, man would die of a great loneliness of the spirit. For whatever happens to the beasts soon happens to man.*

She has written two wildlife care manuals which are in use throughout the United States, Canada, and abroad. Her awards include a California Department of Fish and Game Director's Achievement Award and a Statement of Appreciation from Wildlife Investigations Laboratory for pioneering techniques in the care of fawns.